180 Tunes for Piano Accordion

mel bay prese

by David DiGiuseppe

French Canadian, Cape Breton, Scottish, Shetland, New England, and Southern Old Time Traditions

Complete with fingering, left-hand notation and chord symbols. Appropriate for any G clef instrument.

1 2 3 4 5 6 7 8 9 0

© 2001 BY MEL BAY PUBLICATIONS, INC., PACIFIC, MO 63069.

Visit us on the Web at www.melbay.com — E-mail us at email@melbay.com

Contents

THE TUNES

About the Author

David DiGiuseppe's musical career began at the tender age of three in the local barber shop, where he was often lifted onto a chair and encouraged to sing his favorite songs. At the impressionable age of eight, he was taking accordion lessons, becoming a model student at Petteruti's School of Music in Providence, RI. By twelve, the accordion was in the closet and Beatles' tunes could be heard emanating from his guitar.

In 1984, Mr. DiGiuseppe "rediscovered" the accordion and it's role in folk music. He has since become an accomplished accordionist, focusing on Celtic and American traditional-based music.

Mr. DiGiuseppe has performed professionally since 1978, both as a soloist and with numerous bands. He is a versatile singer, accordionist, mandolinist and Irish cittern player, adept at diverse musical styles. He performs concerts, plays for New England style contra dances, presents educational programs in schools and museums blending history and music, and offers private instruction on accordion and mandolin.

Mr. DiGiuseppe is featured on a number of recordings. His release Welcome to Heaven... (Wizmak Productions, Wingdale, NY) highlights his extraordinary accordion playing on music from Celtic, Parisian and American traditions. Reviewer John O'Regan of Limerick, Ireland wrote, "A player of immense talent and vision, DiGiuseppe is a musician worth encountering".

Visit David DiGiuseppe on the web at http://www.mindspring.com/~daviddg.

The Right Hand

Right hand fingering is suggested for all tunes. A number placed over a note indicates the finger to be used (thumb is #1, little finger is #5). Hand should stay in position when no number appears. For example, if a "1" appears over a C note, it is implied that the second finger sits over the D, third finger over the E, etc. Fingering notation will indicate the next position change.

Fingering is not indicated for passages which are executed earlier in a tune. Use the same fingering as previously shown.

The Left Hand

There are two standard fingering positions for the left hand to choose from:

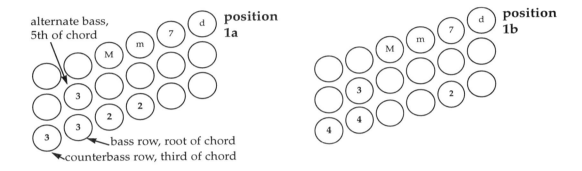

1a) 3rd finger on bass row (root of chord)
    2nd finger on major chord
    2nd finger on minor chord
    3rd finger on alternate bass (next bass note up – the fifth of the chord)
    3rd finger on counterbass row (the 3rd of the chord)

1b) 4th finger on bass row when playing seventh chord
    4th finger on counterbass row when playing seventh chord
    2nd finger on seventh chord

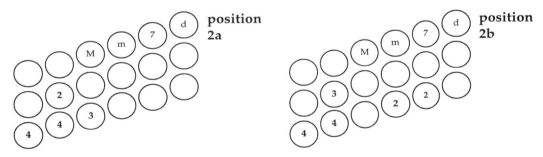

2a) 4th finger on bass row
    3rd finger on major chord
    2nd finger on alternate bass when playing major chord
    4th finger on counter bass row
2b) 2nd finger on minor and seventh chord
    3rd finger on alternate bass when playing minor or seventh chord

*(Note – my personal preference is position 2.)

Bass Diagram

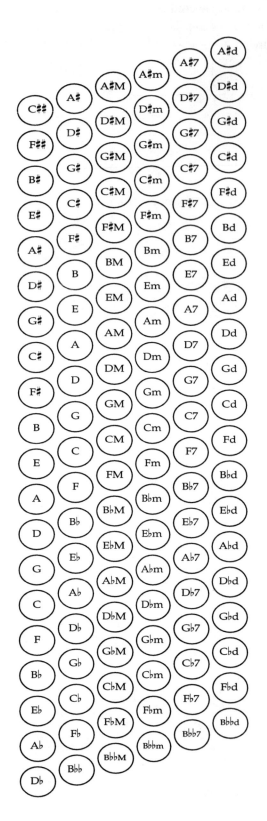

Left hand of the 120 bass accordion

6

Albert's Hornpipe

Scottish Hornpipe

Andy Dejarlis

Cape Breton Jig

Angeline the Baker

Southern Old Time Reel

Angus Chisholm's Favourite

Cape Breton Reel

Aubey Foley's Jig

Cape Breton Jig

Auld Snatwell

Shetland Jig

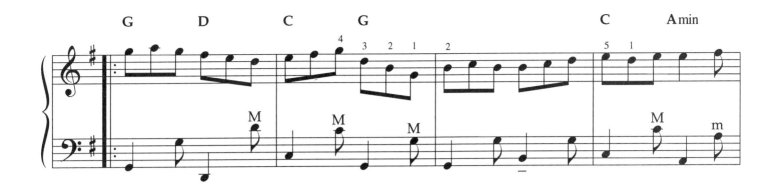

Da Auld Stoer's Back Agen

Shetland Reel

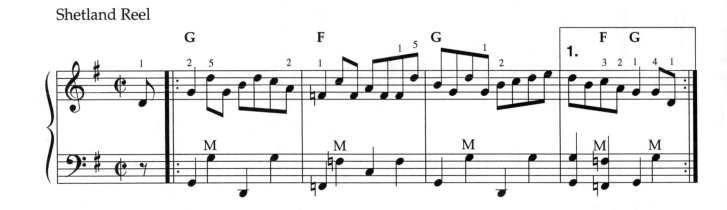

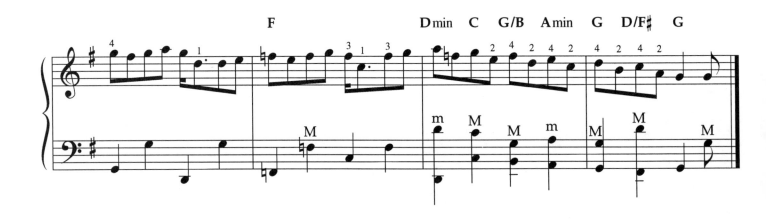

Bachelder's Reel

New England Reel

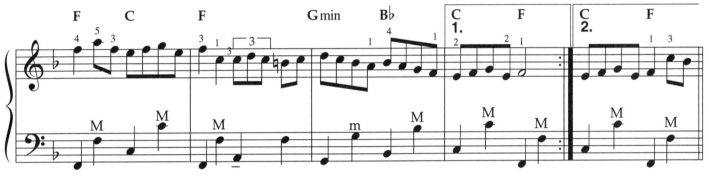

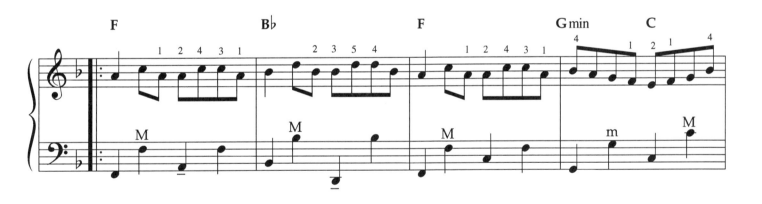

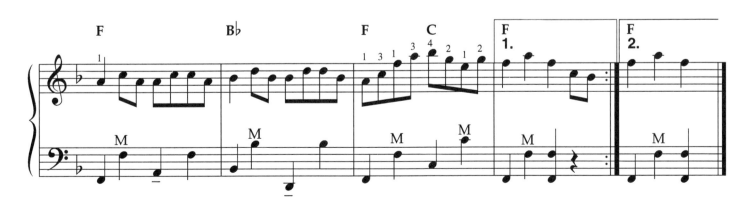

La Bastringue

French Canadian Reel

Bay of Fundy

French Canadian Reel

Beauties of the Ballroom

Cape Breton, Scottish Jig

The Boatman Dance

Southern Old Time Reel

Dan Emmett

Bonaparte Crossing the Rhine

Southern Old Time Reel

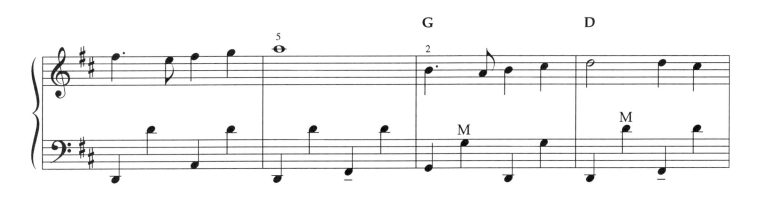

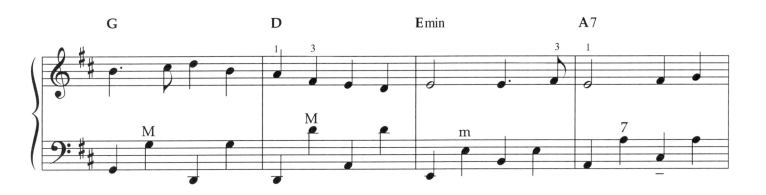

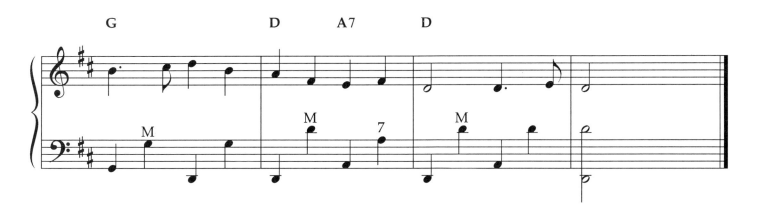

Bonnie Banchory

Scottish Hornpipe

J. Scott Skinner

The Braes O'Tullymet

Scottish Strathspey

Cape North Jig

Cape Breton Jig

Charleston Gals

Southern Old Time Reel

Chorus Jig

New England Reel

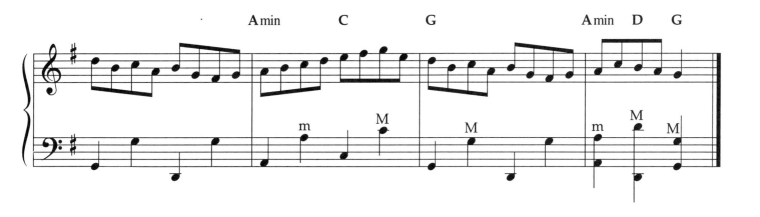

Da Corbie an' da Craw

Shetland Reel

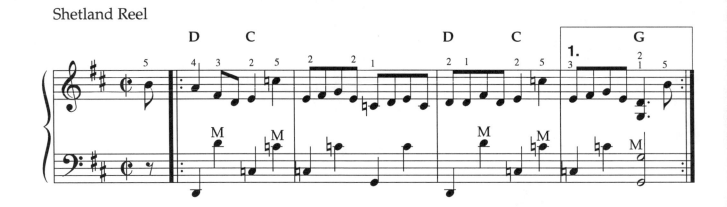

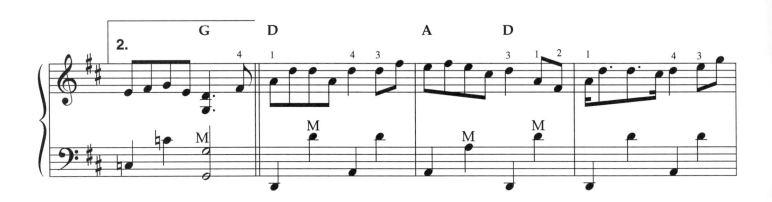

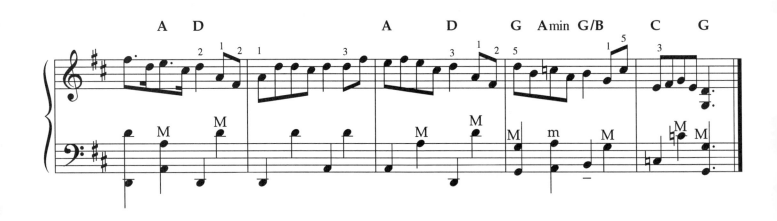

Corn Rigs

Scottish Hornpipe

Cropie's Strathspey

Scottish Strathspey

Dave Marsh's Favourite

Cape Breton Jig

The Devil's Dream

North American, New England Reel

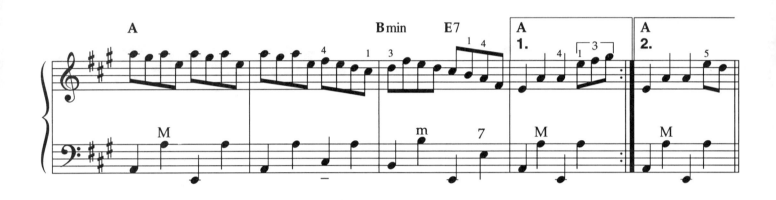

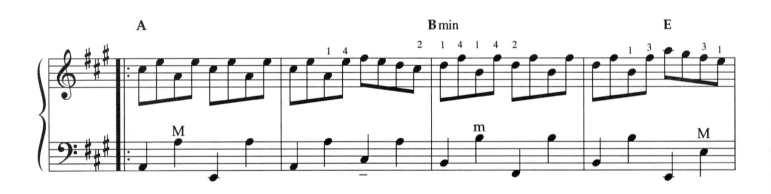

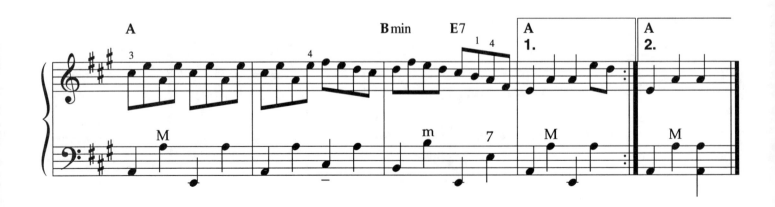

Donald John the Tailor

Cape Breton, Scottish Strathspey

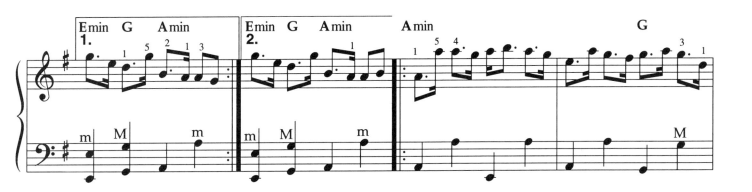

Down the Brae

Scottish March

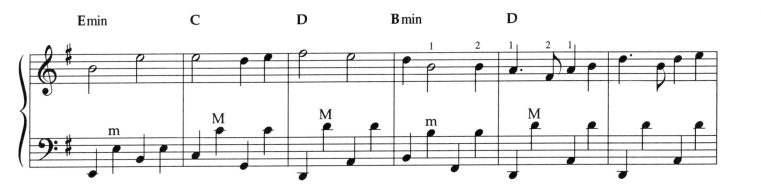

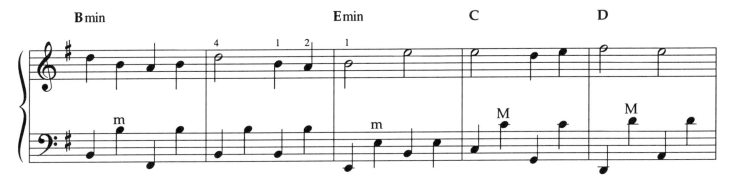

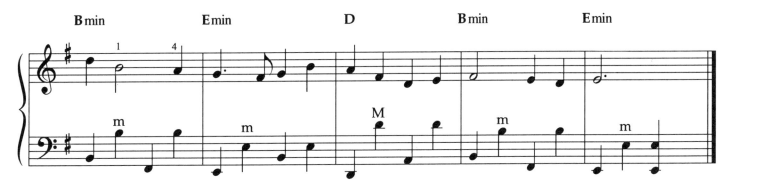

The Drunken Wives of Fochabers

Scottish Strathspey

East Tennessee Blues

Southern Old Time Rag

Elizabeth's Big Coat

Cape Breton Reel

A Finnish Polka

Da Forefit o da Ship

Shetland Reel

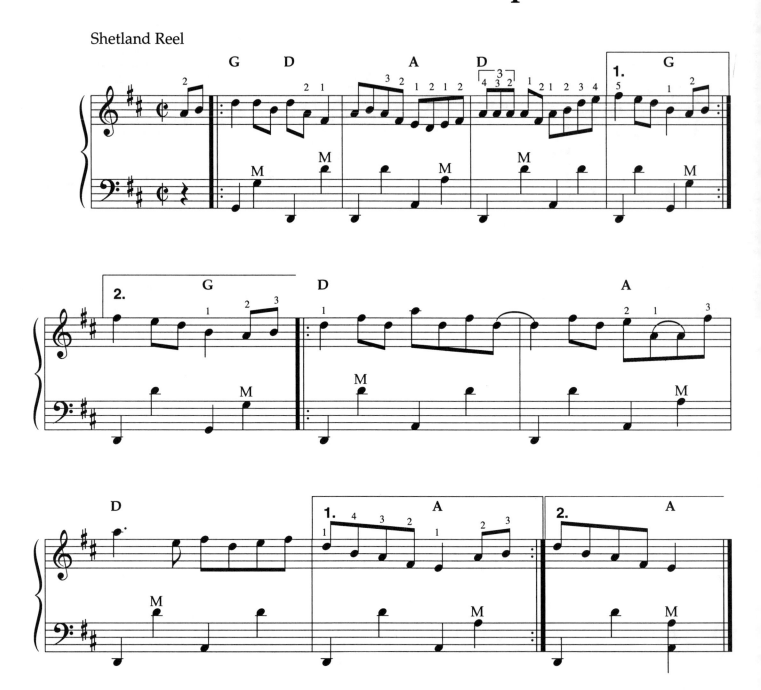

Forester's Hornpipe

New England Hornpipe

Da Galley Watch

Shetland Reel

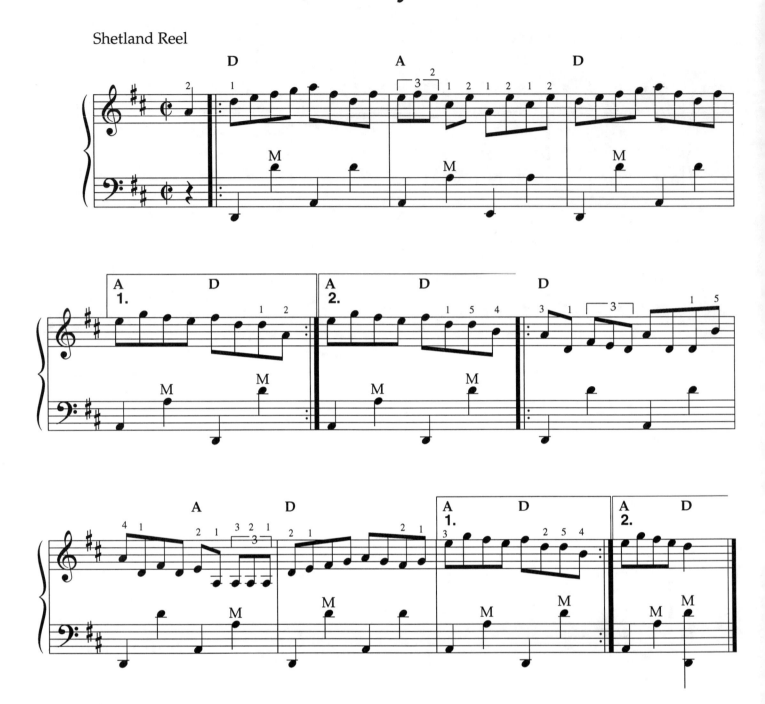

Garster's Dream

Shetland Jig

The Gaspé Reel

French Canadian, New England Reel

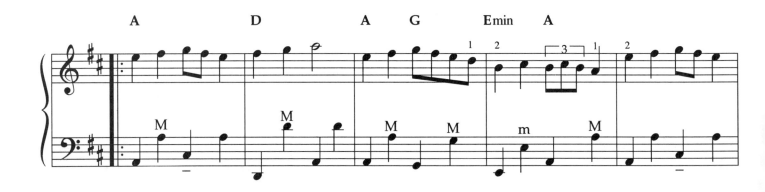

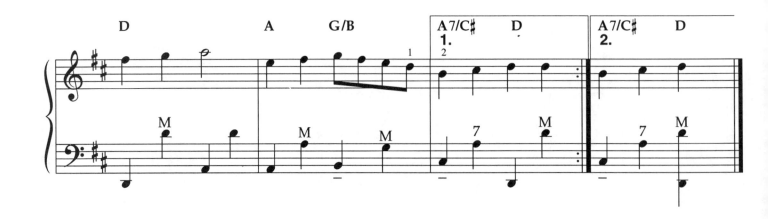

General Drummond

Scottish Reel

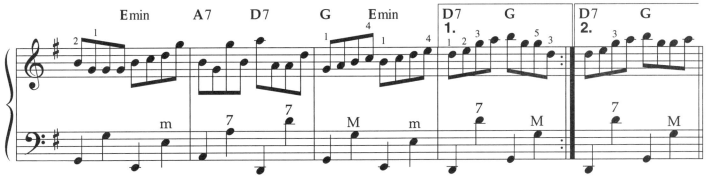

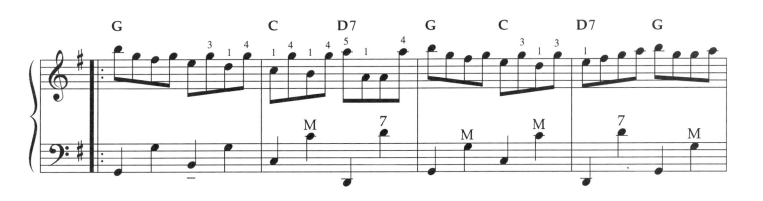

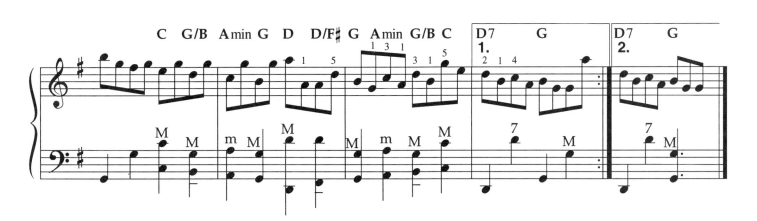

General Stewart

Cape Breton, Scottish Reel

Glasgow Hornpipe

Scottish Hornpipe

La Grande Chaine

French Canadian Reel

La Grondeuse

French Canadian, New England Reel

Growling Old Man, Grumbling Old Woman

New England, French Canadian Reel

Haste to the Wedding

New England, Irish Jig

Highlander's Farewell

Southern Old Time Reel

Highlander's Jig

Cape Breton, Scottish Jig

Indian Reel

French Canadian, New England Reel

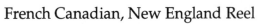

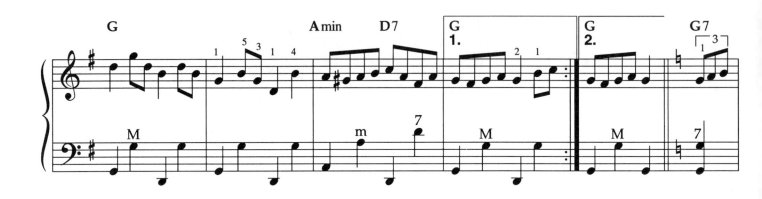

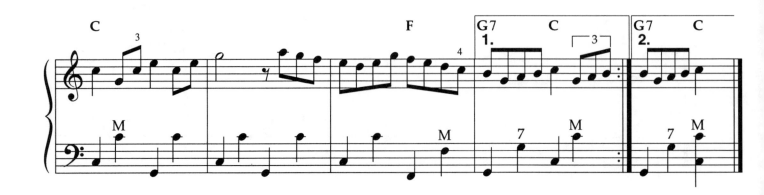

Ingonish Jig

Cape Breton Jig

Jimmy Allen

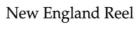

New England Reel

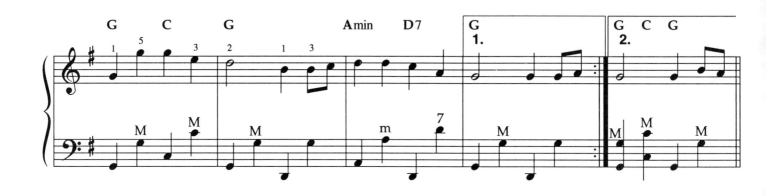

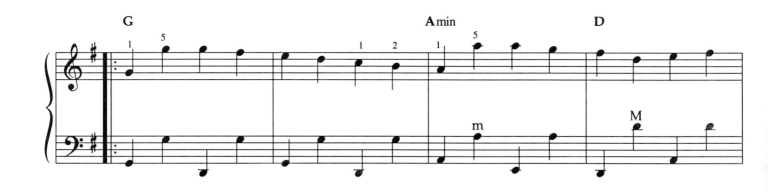

Juliann Johnson

Southern Old Time Reel

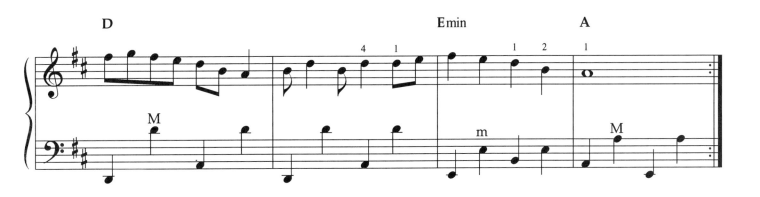

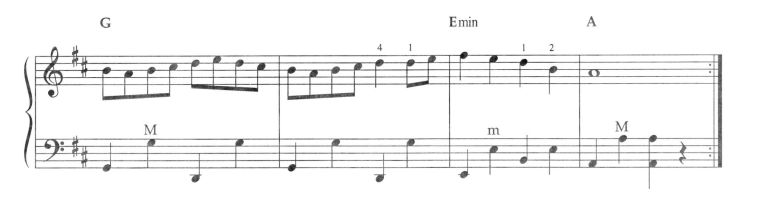

Kiss Her Sweetly

Shetland Reel

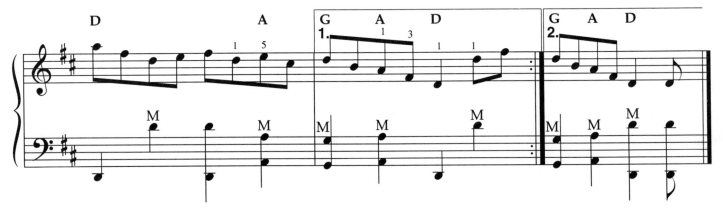

Lady Gordon of Gordonstown

Scottish, Cape Breton Reel

William Morrison

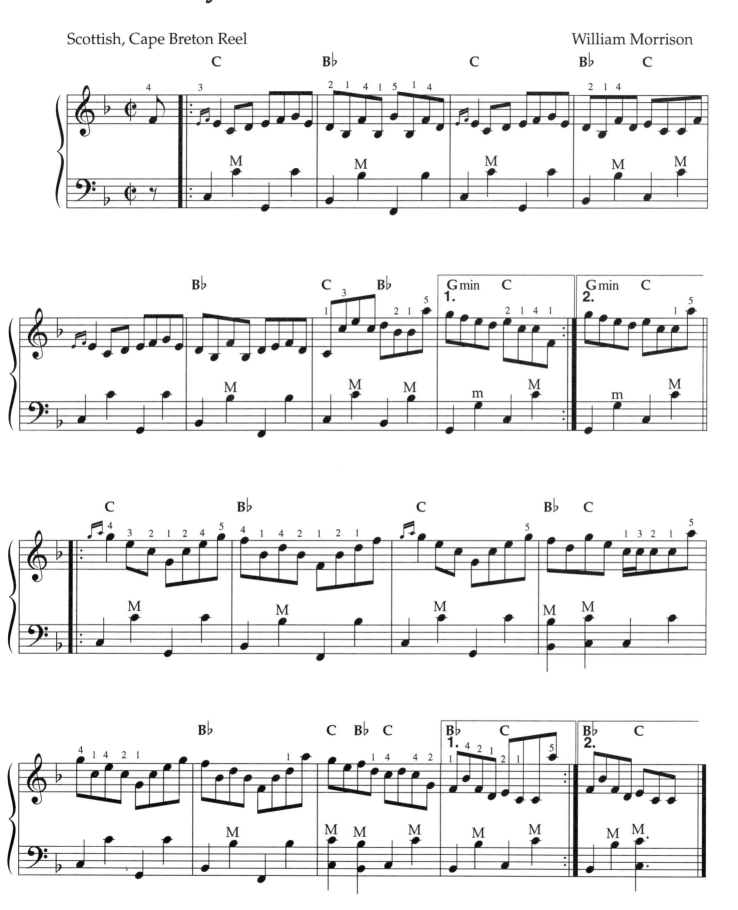

Lady of the Lake

New England Reel

Liza Jane

Southern Old Time Reel

MacBeth's Strathspey

Scottish, Cape Breton Strathspey

Mackilmoyle Reel

French Canadian, New England Reel

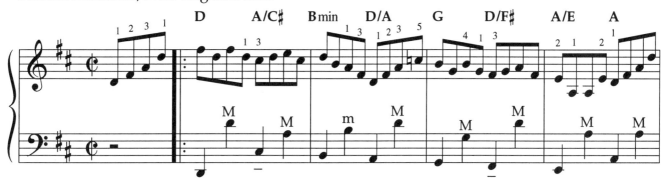

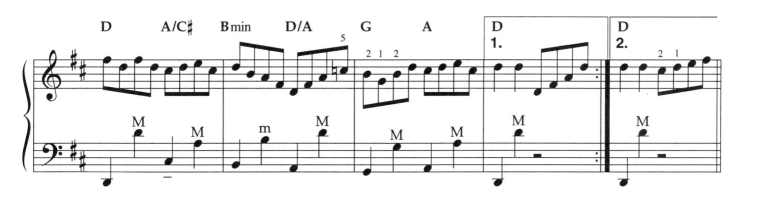

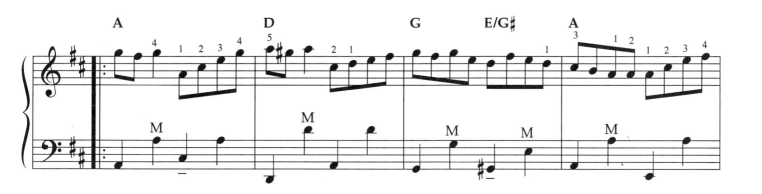

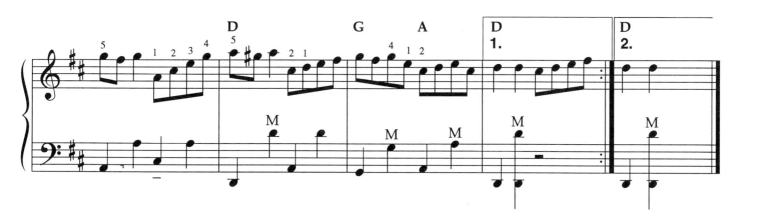

Major Molle's

Scottish, Cape Breton Reel

Andrew Gow

Marcel Martine

Cape Breton Reel

The Mason's Apron

Irish, New England Reel

Mickie Ainsworth

Scottish Hornpipe

Miss Betty Ann Gordon

Cape Breton Reel

Miss Drummond of Perth

Scottish Strathspey

Miss Hannah's Jig

Scottish Jig

William Marshall

Miss McLeod's Reel

Scottish, Irish Reel

Mr. Morison of Bognie

Scottish Jig

William Marshall

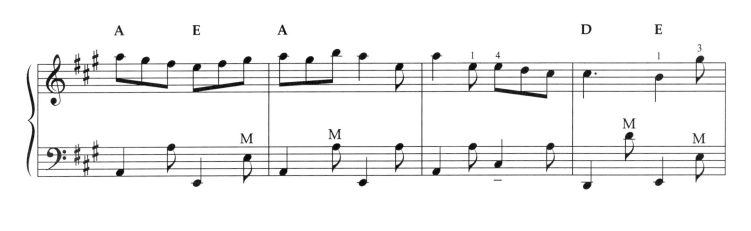

Mouth of the Tobique

French Canadian Reel

Nancy Ann

Southern Old Time Reel

Oot be Est da Vong

Shetland Reel

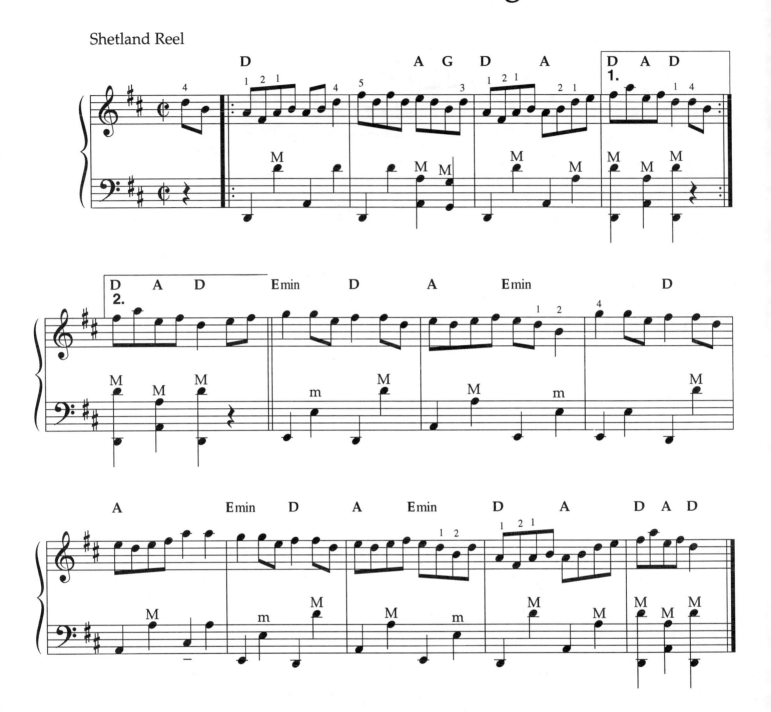

Opera Reel

New England Reel

Pays de Haut

French Canadian, New England Reel

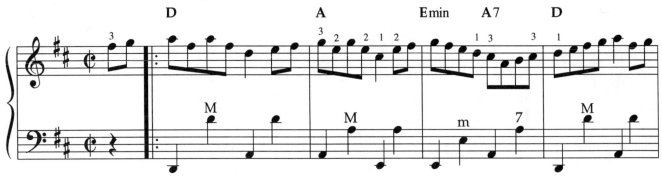

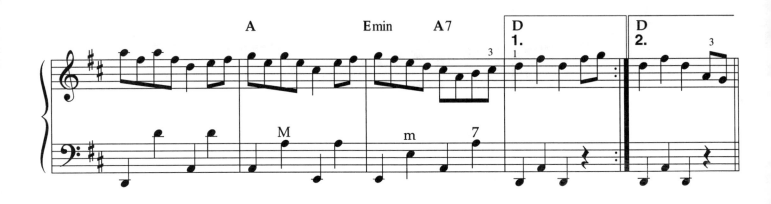

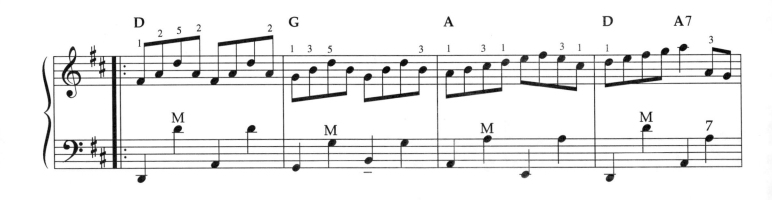

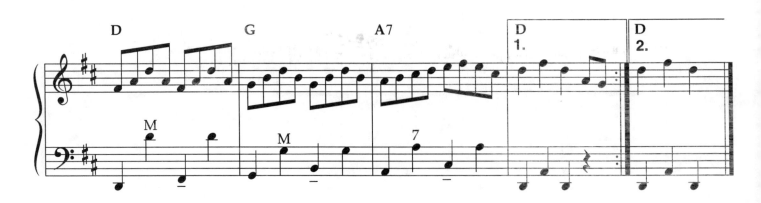

Peter Francisco

Southern Old Time Reel

Pit Hame da Borrowed Claes

Shetland Reel

Po' Liza

Southern Old Time Reel

President Garfield's Hornpipe

New England Hornpipe

Quindaro Hornpipe

New England Hornpipe

Reconciliation

Irish, New England Reel

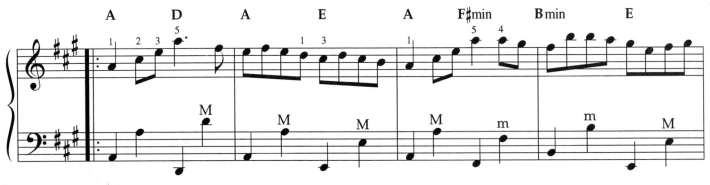

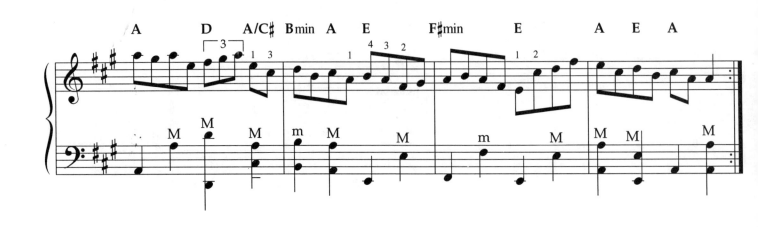

Reel Alouette

French Canadian Reel

Reel de Beatrice

French Canadian Reel

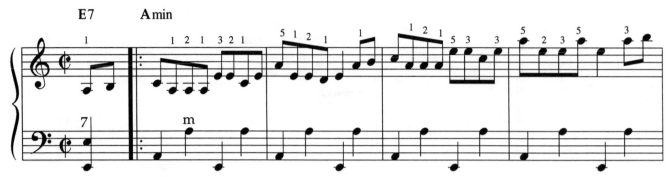

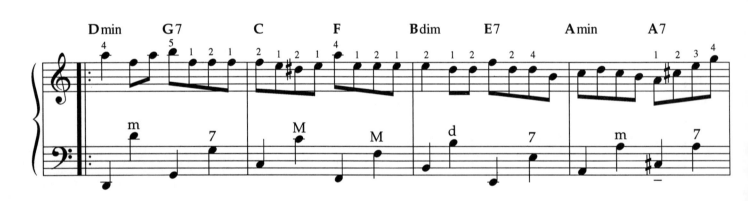

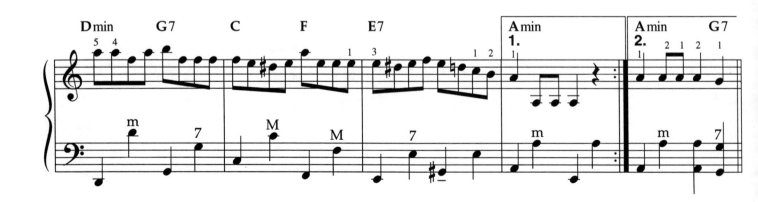

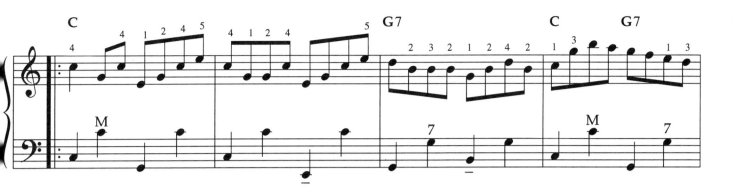

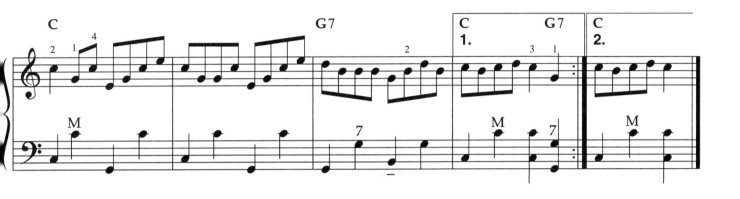

Reel de Montreal

French Canadian, New England Reel

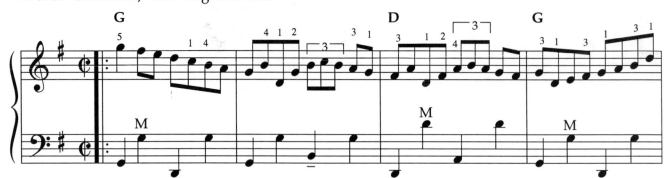

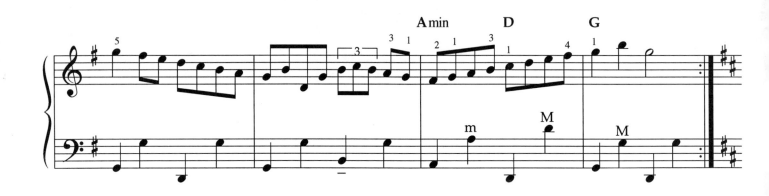

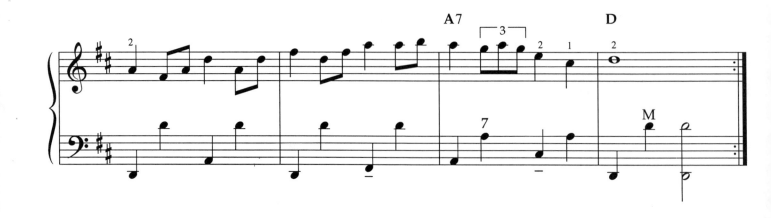

Reel des Ouviers

(Walker St.)

French Canadian, New England Reel

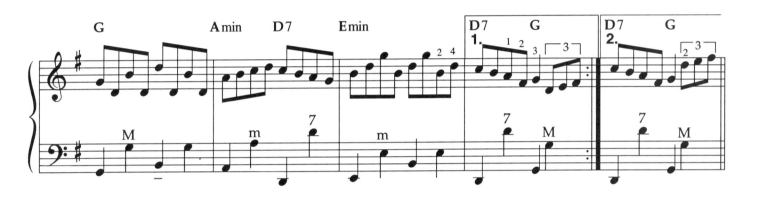

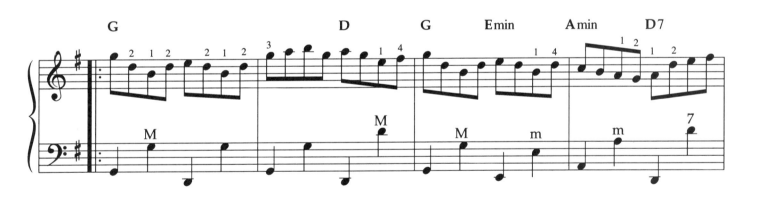

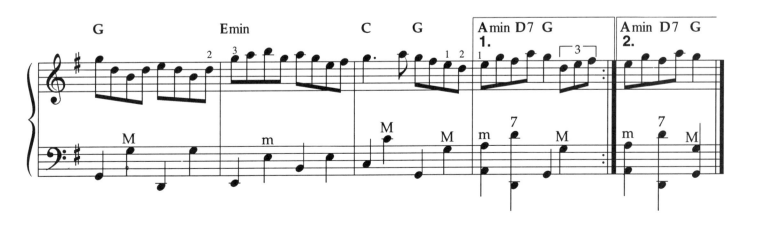

Reel St. Antoine

French Canadian Reel

Reel St. Jean

French Canadian Reel

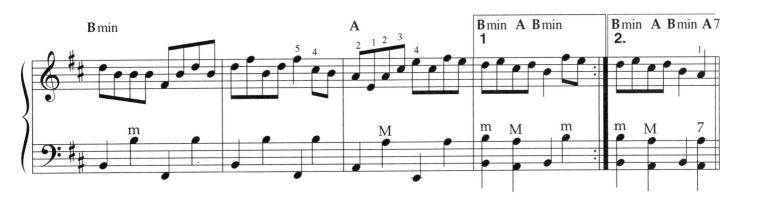

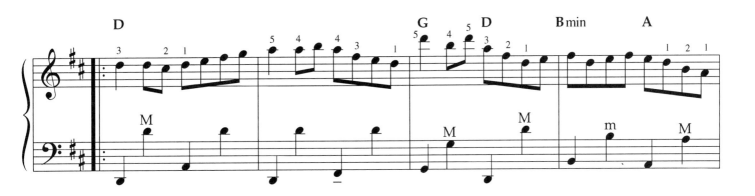

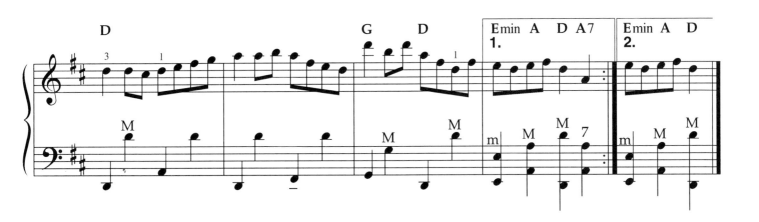

Rickett's Hornpipe

New England Hornpipe

Rock the Cradle Joe

Southern Old Time Reel

Ross's Reel No. 4

New England Reel

Sandy Boys

Southern Old Time Reel

Da Scalloway Lasses

Shetland Reel

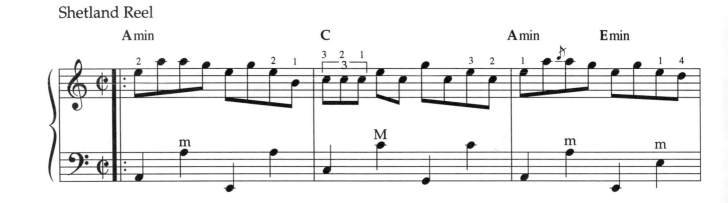

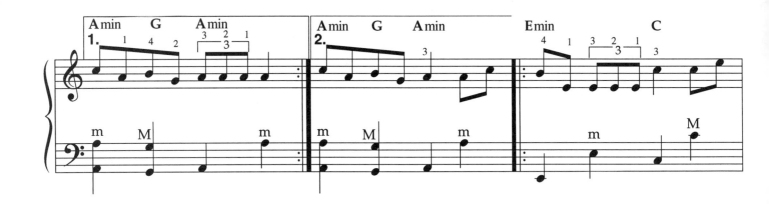

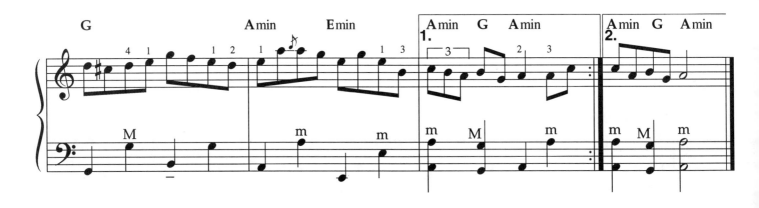

Seneca Square Dance

Southern Old Time Reel

Da Shaalds O' Foula

Shetland Jig

Shenandoah Falls

Southern Old Time Reel

Sillocks and Tatties

Shetland Reel

Smith's Hornpipe

Scottish Hornpipe

Spey the Spate

Scottish, Cape Breton Reel

J. Scott Skinner

Spootiskerry

Shetland, New England Reel

Spotted Pony

Southern Old Time Reel

Square da Mizzen

Shetland Reel

St. Anne's Reel

French Canadian Reel

Staten Island Hornpipe

New England Hornpipe

Tam's Grey Mare

Cape Breton, Scottish Reel

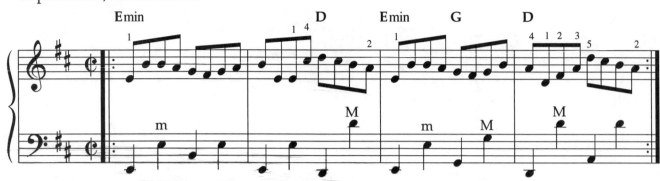

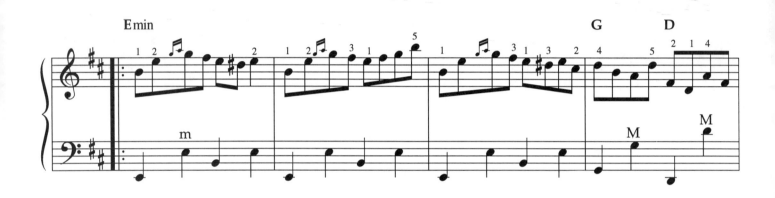

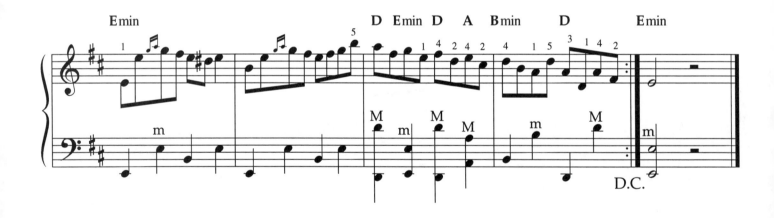

Timour the Tartar

(Peter Street)

Scottish Reel

J. Scott Skinner

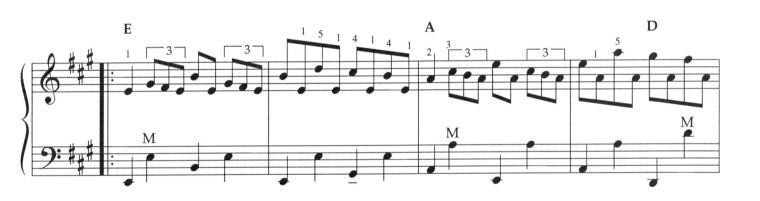

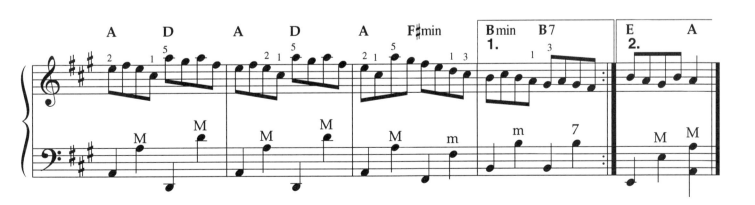

Da Underhill

Shetland Reel

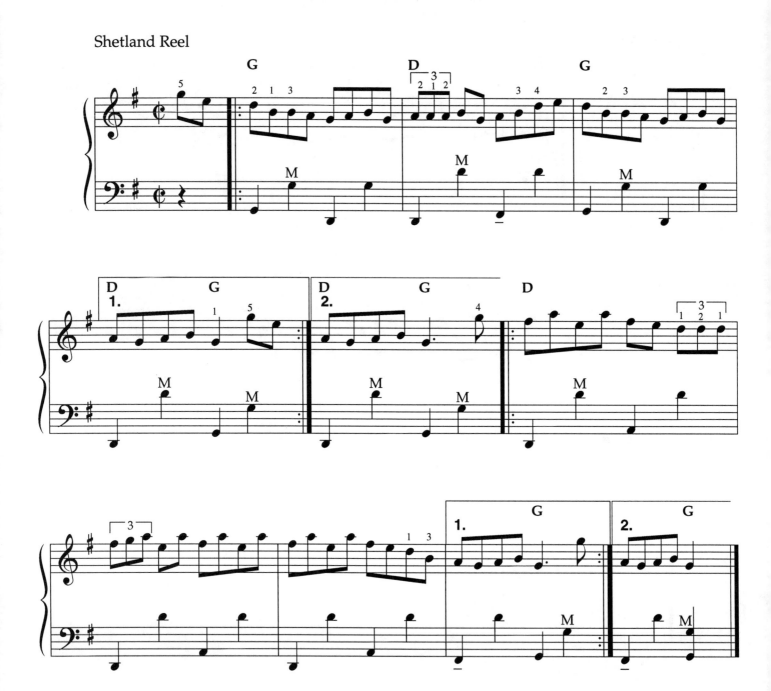

West Fork Gals

Southern Old Time Reel

Woodchopper's Reel

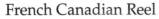

French Canadian Reel

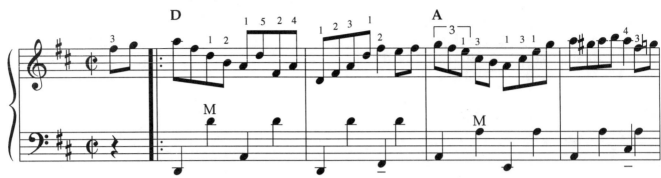

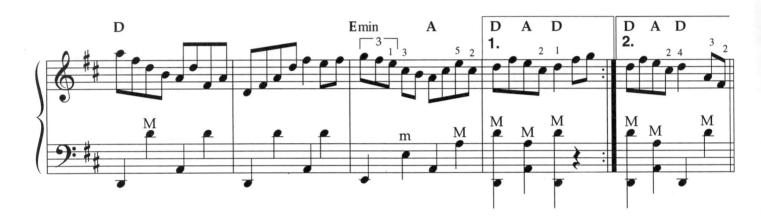

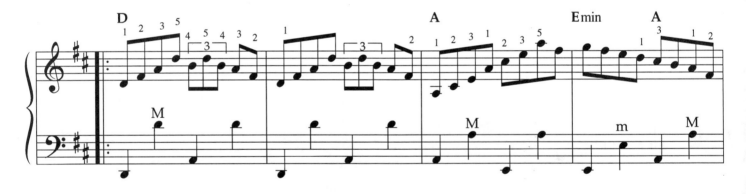

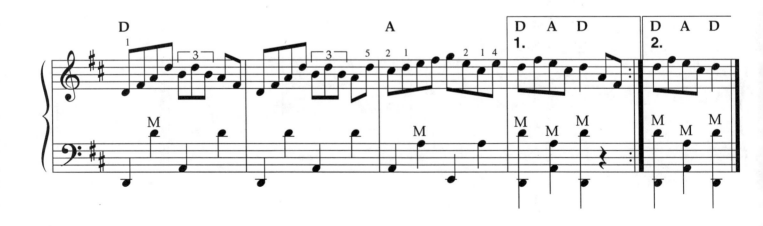

The Best of Smashing Pumpkins for Easy Guitar

MCA Music Limited

Exclusive Distributors:
Music Sales Limited
8/9 Frith Street,
London W1V 5TZ, England.
Music Sales Pty Limited
120 Rothschild Avenue
Rosebery, NSW 2018,
Australia.

Order No.AM944658
ISBN 0-7119-6660-5
This book © Copyright 1997 by MCA Music Limited

Music arranged by Louis Martinez
Cover design by **nim** *Design Consultants*

Printed in Great Britain by
Printwise (Haverhill) Limited, Haverhill, Suffolk

Your Guarantee of Quality

As publishers, we strive to produce every book to the highest commercial standards. The book has been carefully designed to minimise awkward page turns and to make playing from it a real pleasure. Particular care has been given to specifying acid-free, neutral-sized paper made from pulps which have not been elemental chlorine bleached. This pulp is from farmed sustainable forests and was produced with special regard for the environment. Throughout, the printing and binding have been planned to ensure a sturdy, attractive publication which should give years of enjoyment. If your copy fails to meet our high standards, please inform us and we will gladly replace it.

Music Sales' complete catalogue describes thousands of titles and is available in full colour sections by subject, direct from Music Sales Limited. Please state your areas of interest and send a cheque/postal order for £1.50 for postage to: Music Sales Limited, Newmarket Road, Bury St. Edmunds, Suffolk IP33 3YB.

Bullet With Butterfly Wings

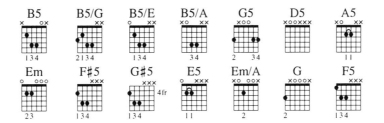

Bullet with Butterfly Wings – 6 – 1
PG9703

3

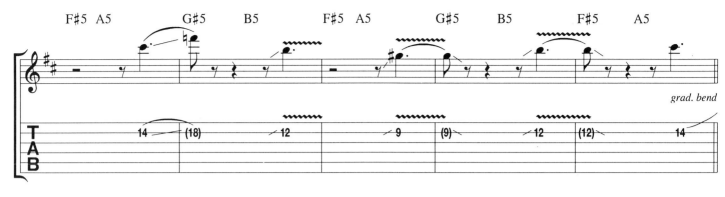

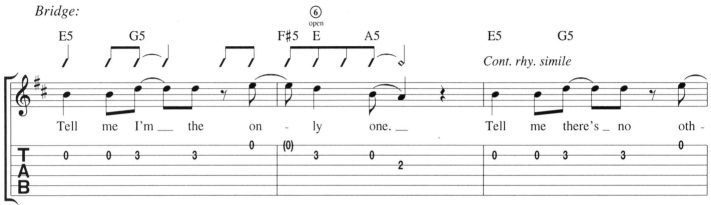

Bridge:

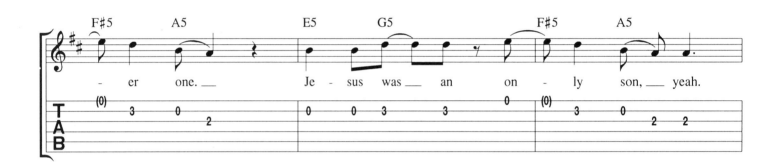

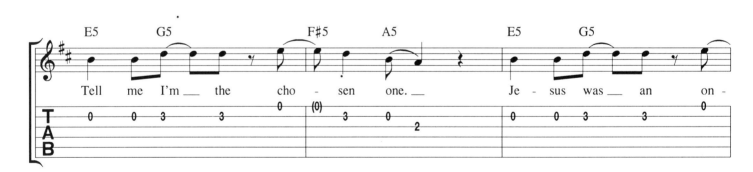

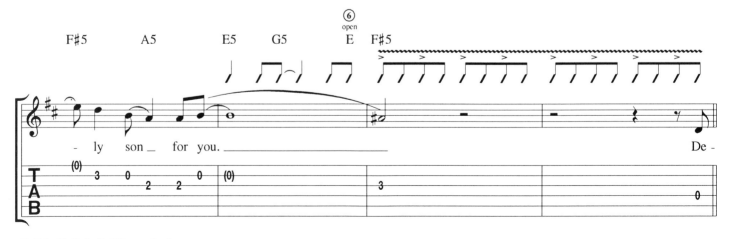

Bullet with Butterfly Wings – 6 – 4
PG9703

6

Breakdown Chorus:

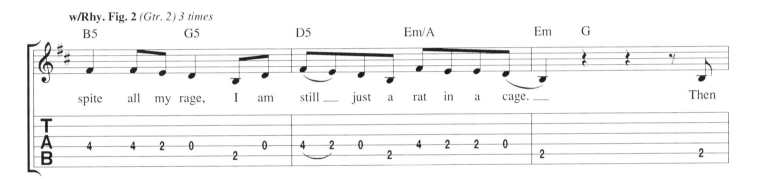

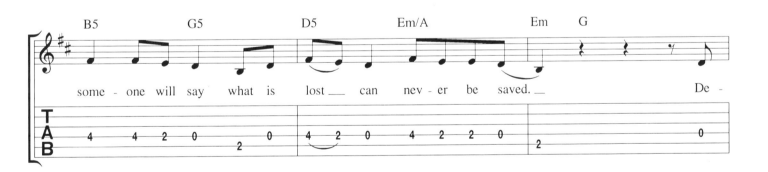

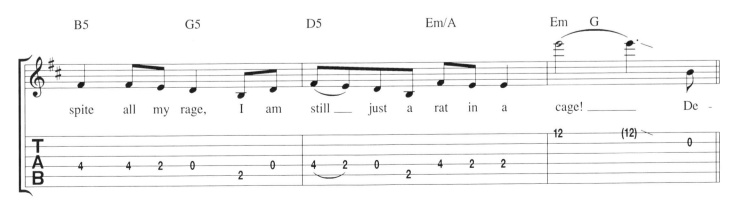

Out-Chorus:

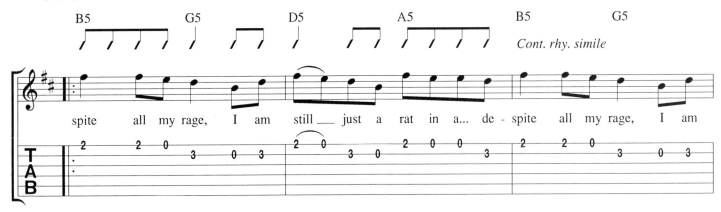

Outro/ Chorus:
Despite all my rage, I am still just a rat in a...
Despite all my rage, I am still just a rat in a...
Despite all my rage, I am still just a rat in a cage!
Tell me I'm the only one.
Tell me there's no other one.
Jesus was an only son for you.
And I still believe that I cannot be saved.
And I still believe that I cannot be saved.
And I still believe that I cannot be saved.
And I still believe that I cannot be saved.

Cupid De Locke

Words & Music by Billy Corgan

© Copyright 1995 MCA Music Limited, 77 Fulham Palace Road, London W6 8JA.
All Rights Reserved. International Copyright Secured.

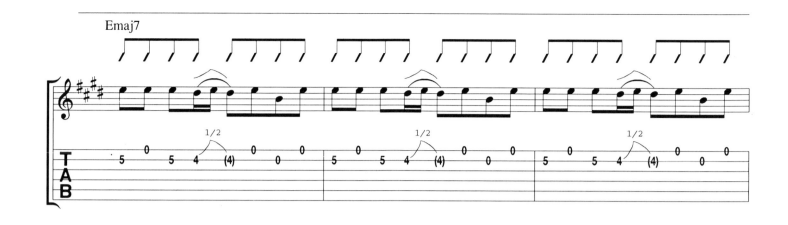

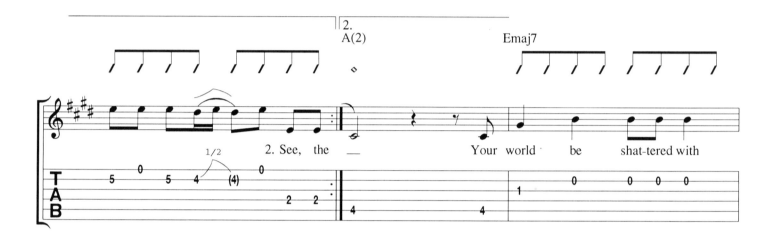

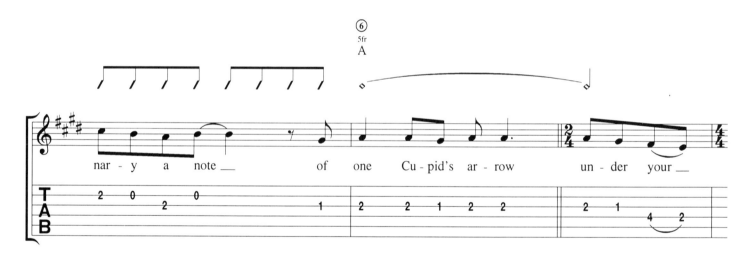

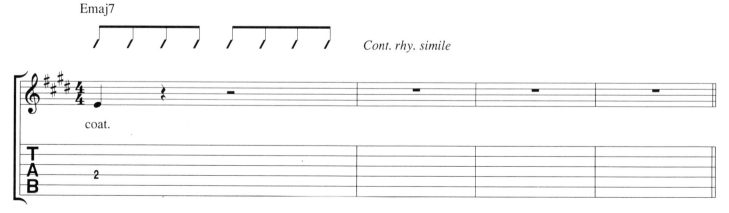

Cupid De Locke – 3 – 2
PG9703

10

Outro:
w/recitation

Sing, _ yeah, _ yeah, _ yeah. _   Sing, _ yeah, _ yeah, _ yeah. _

Sing, __ yeah, __ yeah, __ yeah.   Sing, __ yeah, __ yeah, __ yeah.

Sing, __ yeah, __ yeah, __ yeah.   Sing, __ yeah, __ yeah, __ yeah.

Gtr. 2

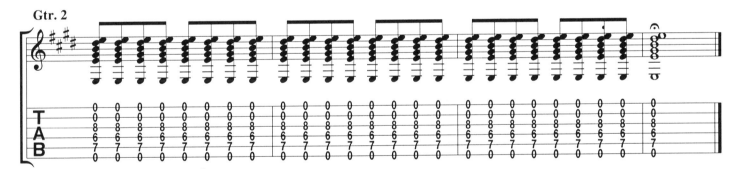

Recitation:
And in the land of star-crossed lovers,
And barren-hearted wanderers,
Forever lost in forsaken missives and Satan's pull,
We seek the unseekable and we speak the unspeakable,
Our hopes dead, gathering dust to dust
In faith, in compassion and in love.

Verse 2:
See, the devil may do as the devil may care.
He loves none sweeter than sweeter the dare.
Her mouth the mischief he doth seek.
Her heart the captive of which he speaks.

Chorus 2:
So note all ye lovers in love with the sound.
Your world be shattered with nary a note
Of one Cupid's arrow under your coat.

Cherub Rock

Words & Music by Billy Corgan

long __ as __ there's some mon - ey? __   Who   wants __ the hon   -

ey? __

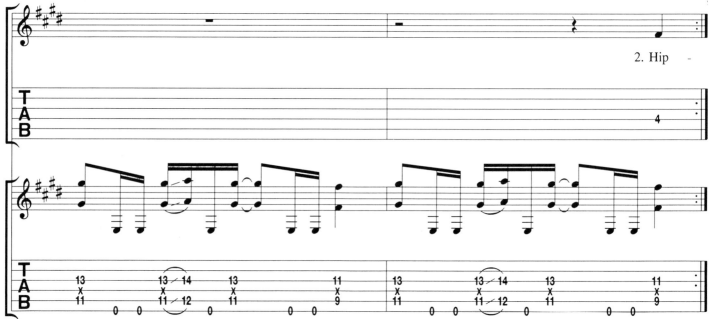

2. Hip -

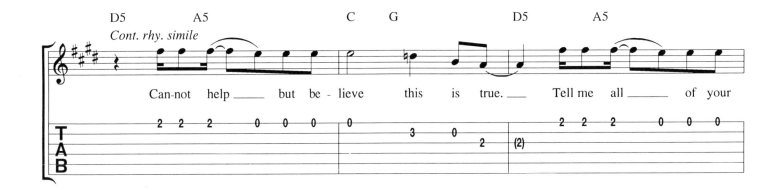

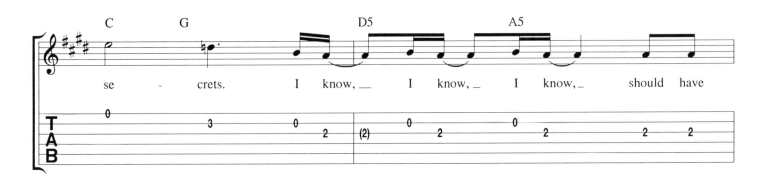

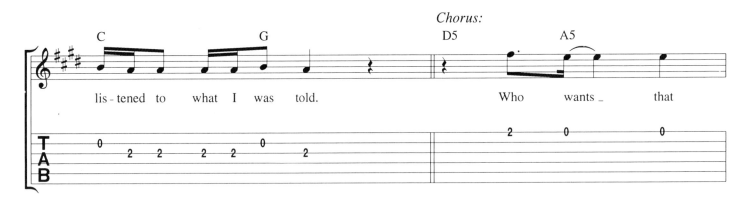

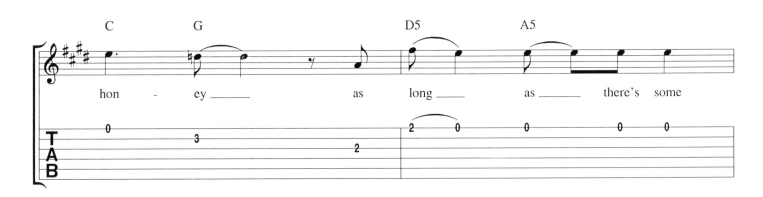

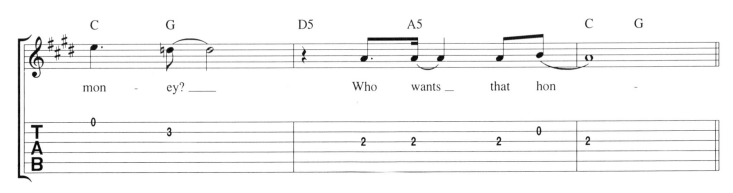

Cherub Rock – 6 – 5
PG9703

16

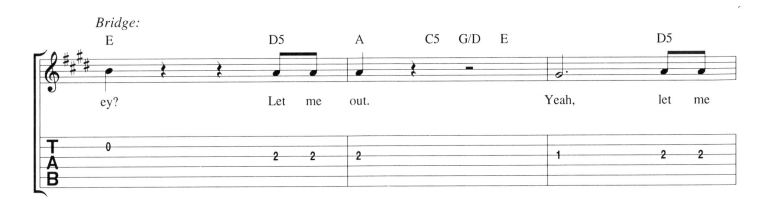

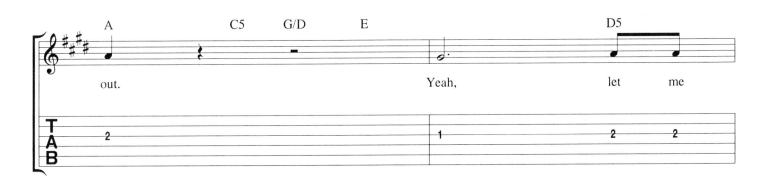

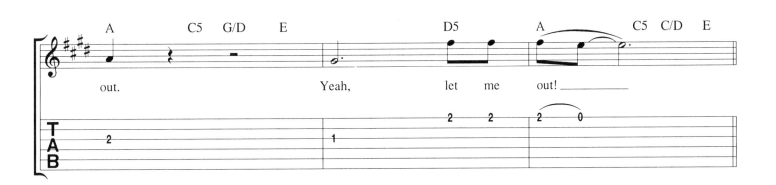

Here is No Why

Words & Music by Billy Corgan

© Copyright 1995 MCA Music Limited, 77 Fulham Palace Road, London W6 8JA.
All Rights Reserved. International Copyright Secured.

Tune down 1/2 step:
⑥= Eb   ③= Gb
⑤= Ab   ②= Bb
④= Db   ①= Eb

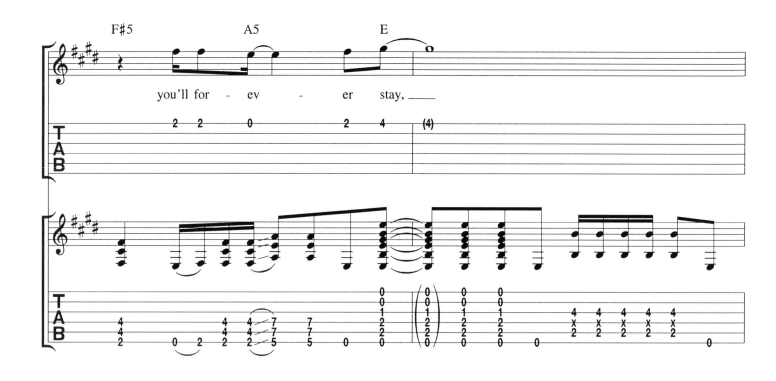

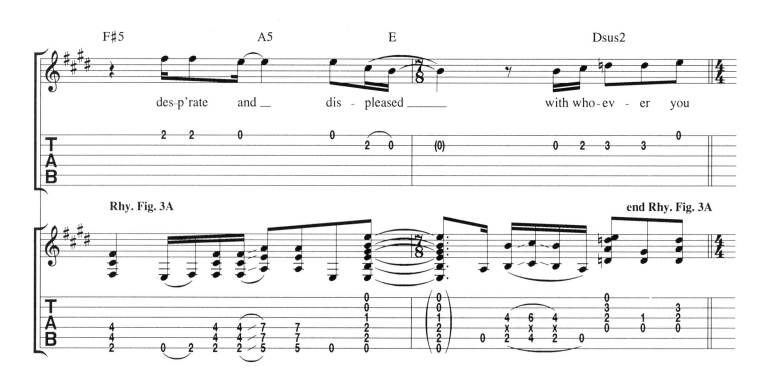

Verse 2:

w/Rhy. Fig. 2 *(Gtr. 2)*

Some-where, he pulls his hair __ down o - ver a frown - ing smile. __

A hid-den dia - mond you can - not find. A

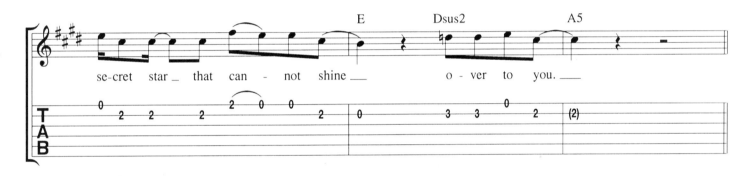

se-cret star __ that can - not shine __ o - ver to you. __

𝄋 *Pre-Chorus:*

1. Way the king of gloom __
2. And if you're giv - ing in, __

Chorus 2:

w/Rhy. Fig. 3 *(Gtr. 2) 3 times*

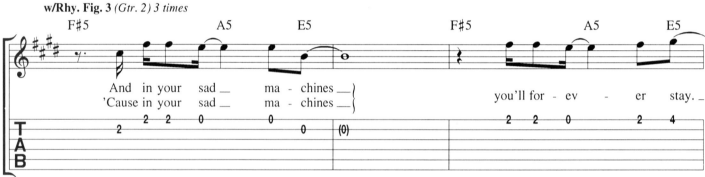

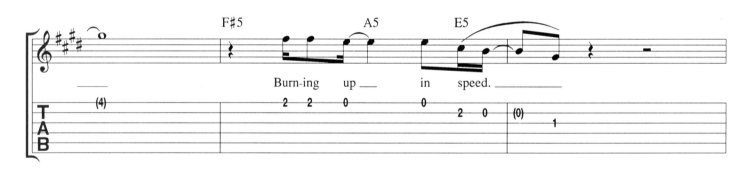

To Coda ⊕

w/Rhy. Fig. 3A *(Gtr. 2)*

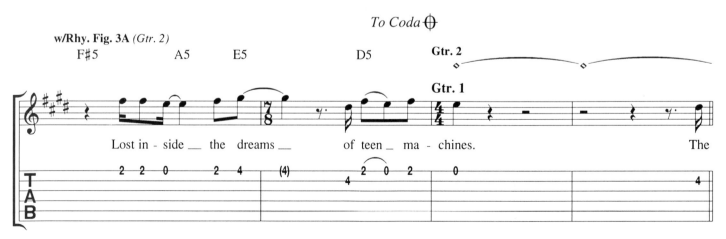

Love

Words & Music by Billy Corgan

© Copyright 1995 MCA Music Limited, 77 Fulham Palace Road, London W6 8JA.

All Rights Reserved. International Copyright Secured.

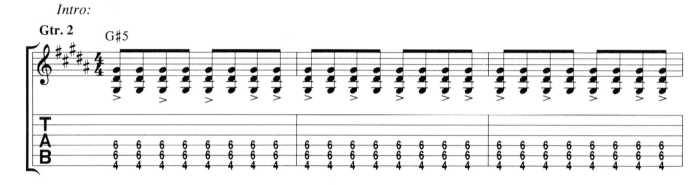

Moderate rock ♩ = 96

Intro:

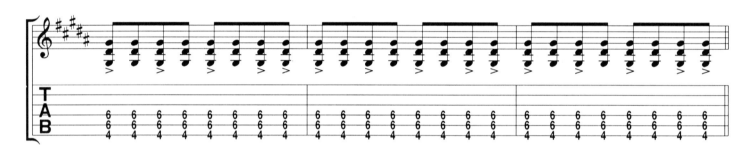

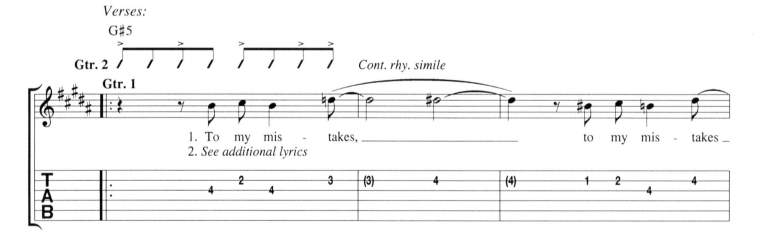

Verses:

1. To my mis - takes, _____ to my mis - takes _____
2. *See additional lyrics*

Cont. rhy. simile

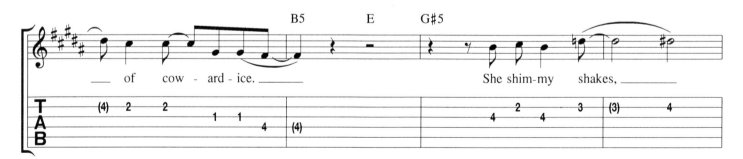

_____ of cow - ard - ice. _____ She shim - my shakes, _____

Love – 6 – 1
PG9703

24

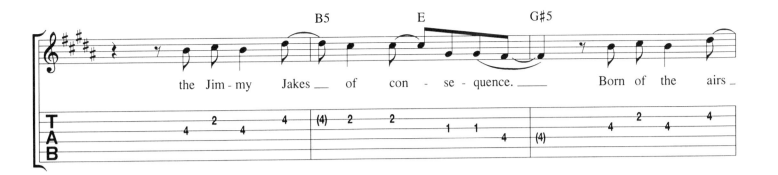

Pre-Chorus 1:

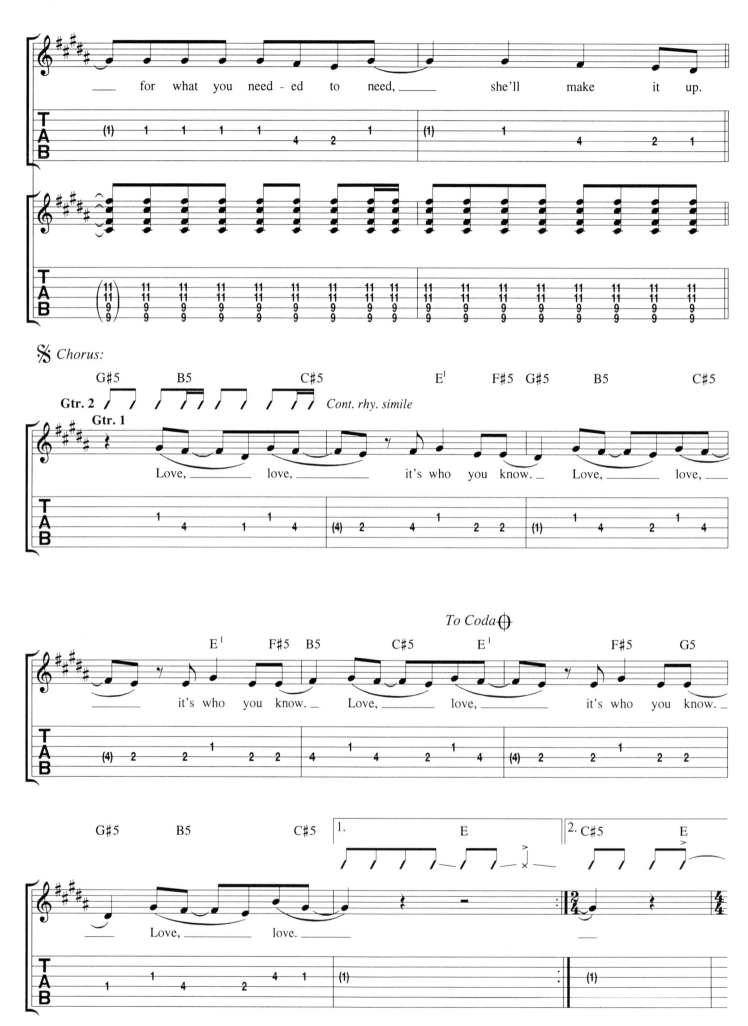

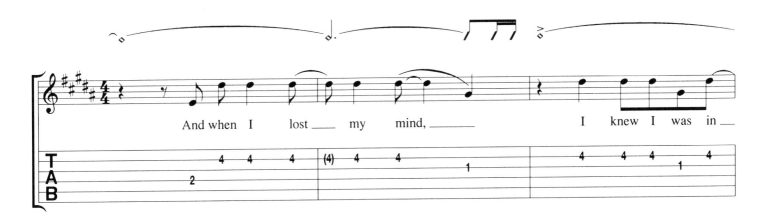

And when I lost___ my mind,_____ I knew I was in___

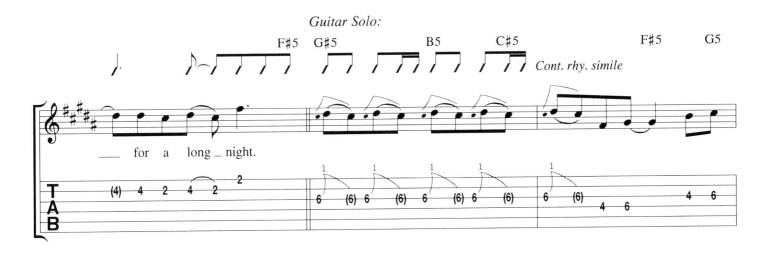

Guitar Solo:

F#5 G#5   B5   C#5   F#5   G5

Cont. rhy. simile

___ for a long _ night.

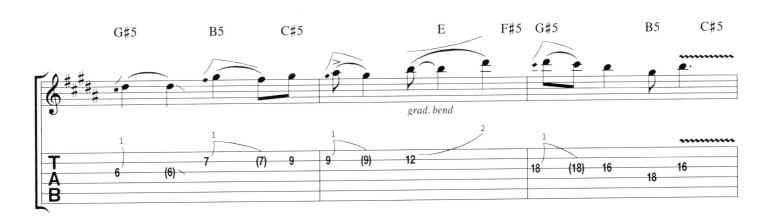

G#5   B5   C#5   E   F#5 G#5   B5   C#5

grad. bend

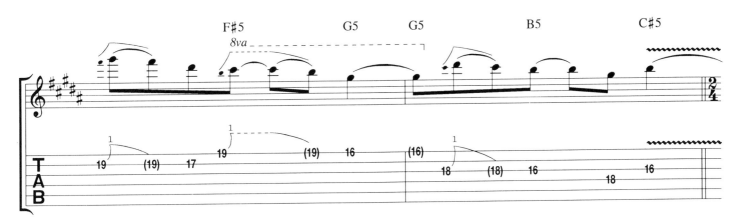

F#5   G5   G5   B5   C#5

8va

Love – 6 – 4
PG9703

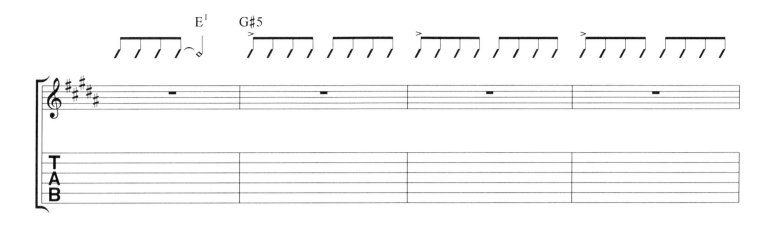

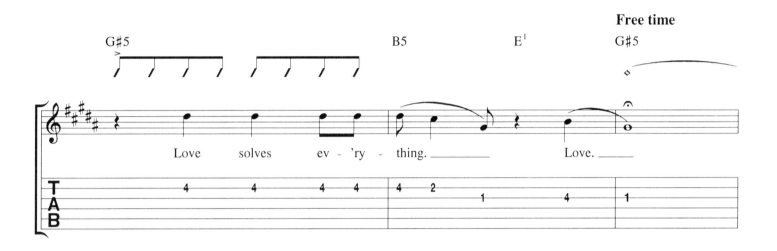

Love   solves   ev - 'ry - thing. _____   Love. _____

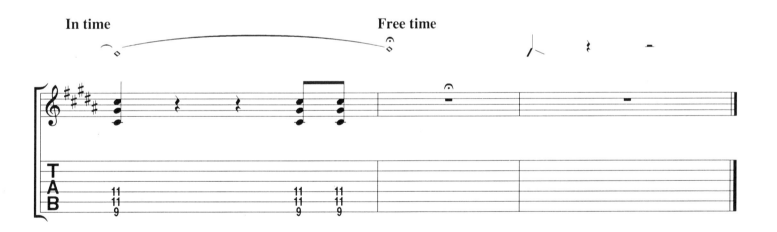

Verse 2:
Machine gun blues, her vacant rush is so steel.
I'm unaware, lost inside your visions.
I got mine too over, I got mine and I got you.
'Cause I know you, you're love.

Love – 6 – 6
PG9703

Disarm

Words & Music by Billy Corgan

© Copyright 1993 MCA Music Limited, 77 Fulham Palace Road, London W6 8JA.

All Rights Reserved. International Copyright Secured.

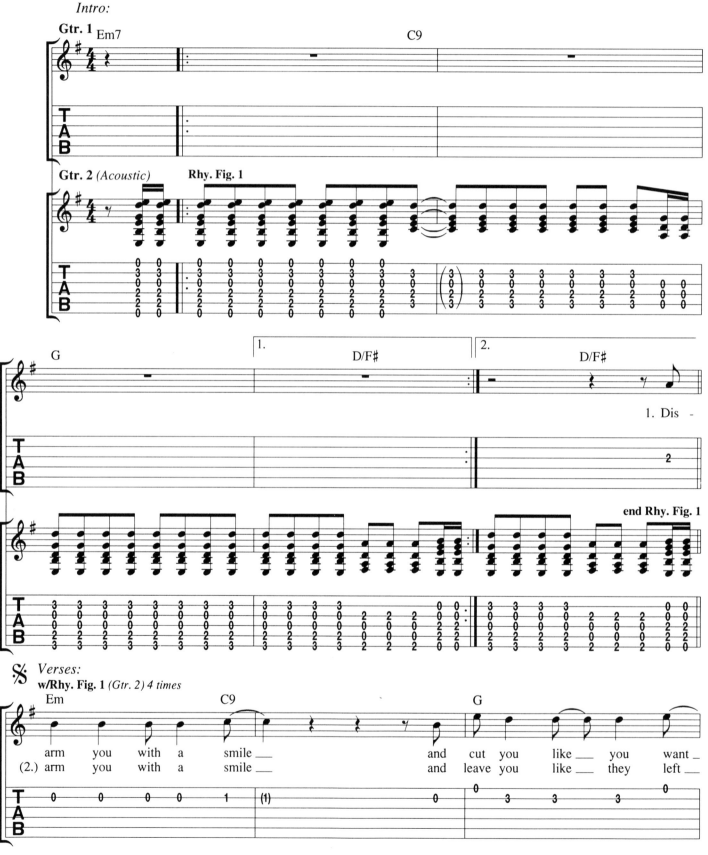

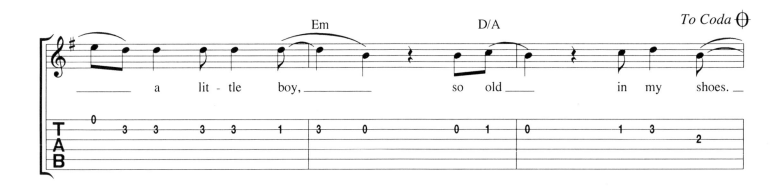

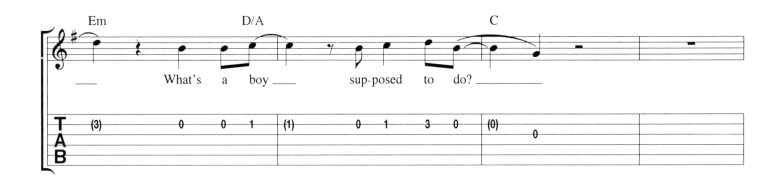

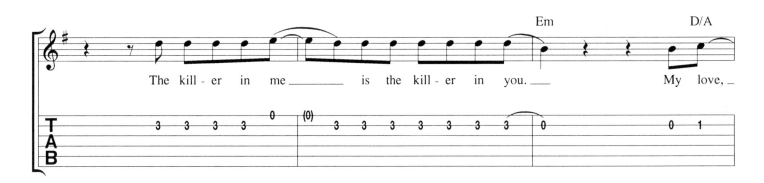

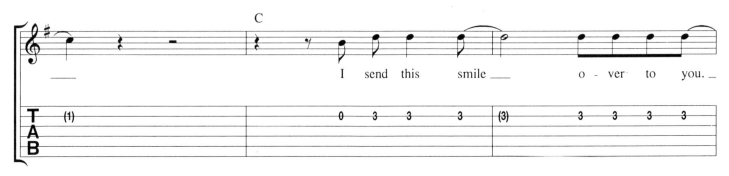

Disarm – 5 – 3
PG9703

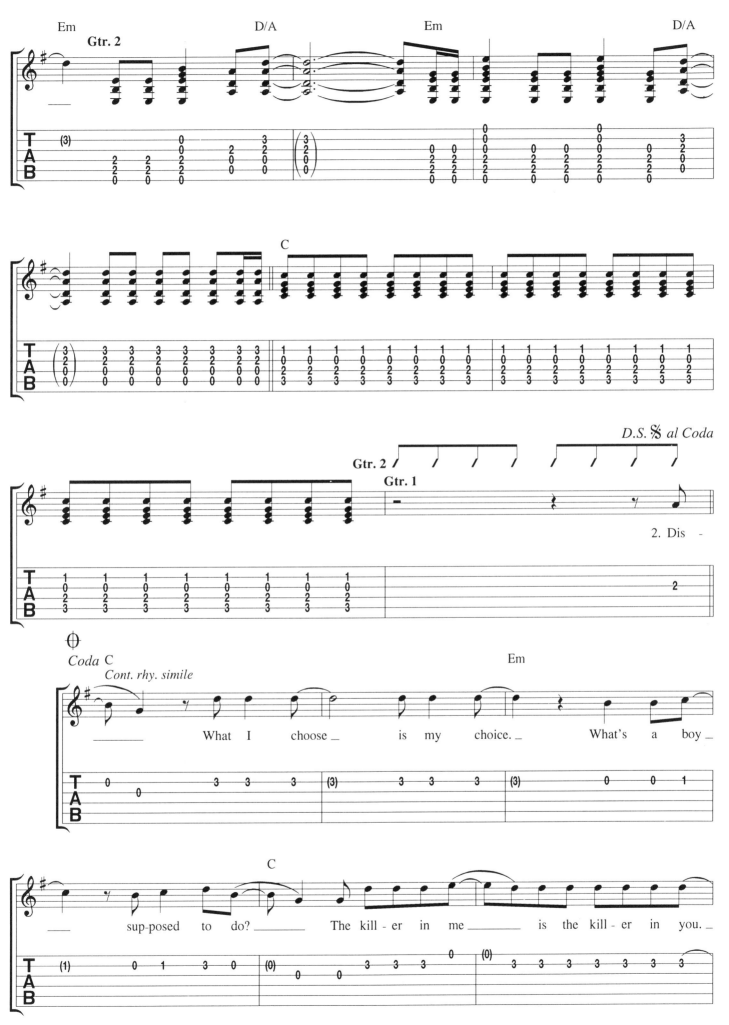

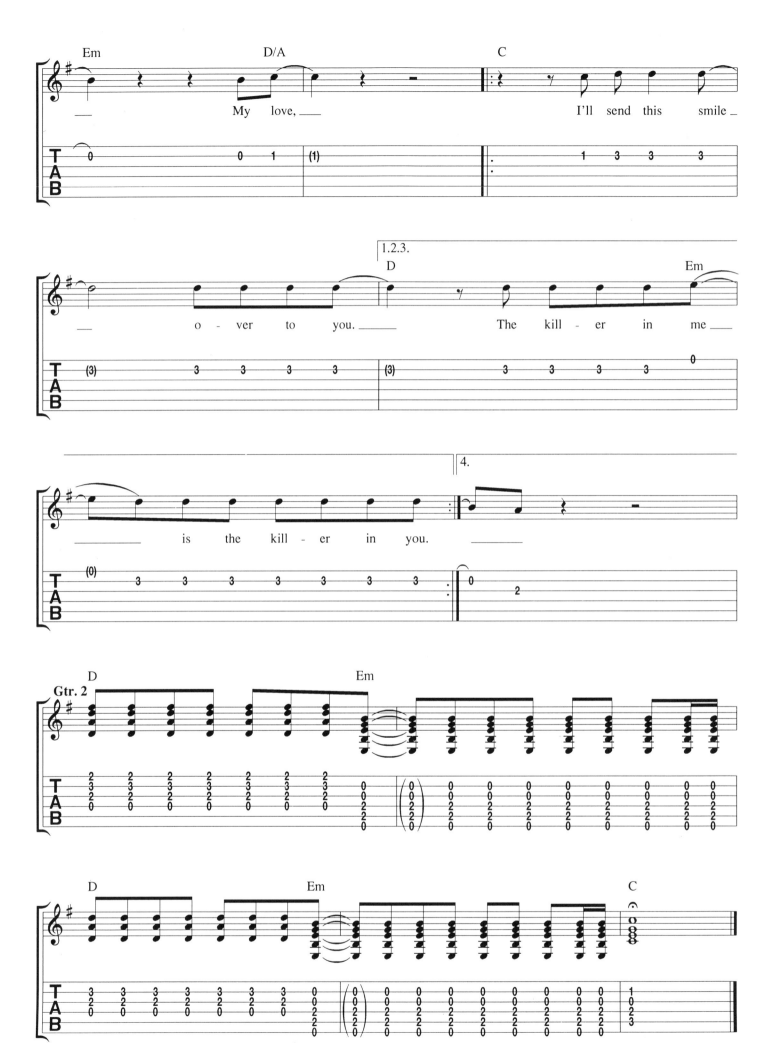

Words & Music by Billy Corgan

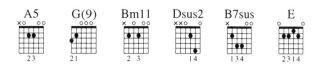

Tune down 1/2 step:

⑥ = E♭   ③ = G♭

⑤ = A♭   ② = A♭

④ = D♭   ① = D♭

*This song uses an altered tuning, the "B" (②) string is tuned down a whole-step to "A." Billy uses simple chord shapes in combination with the ringing open ① and ② strings (E and A) to produce some beautiful chord sounds.

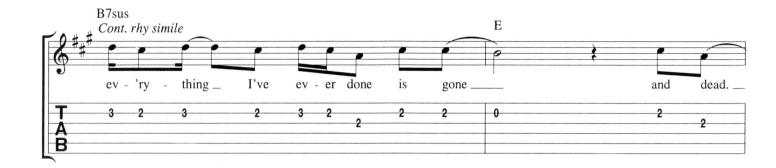

w/Rhy. Fig. 1 *(Gtr. 2) 3 times*   Chorus:

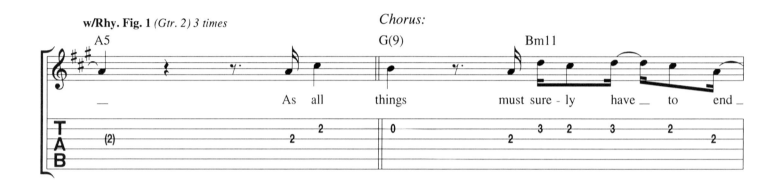

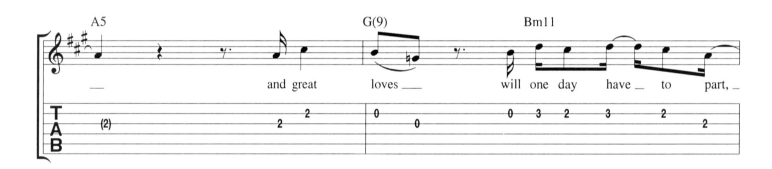

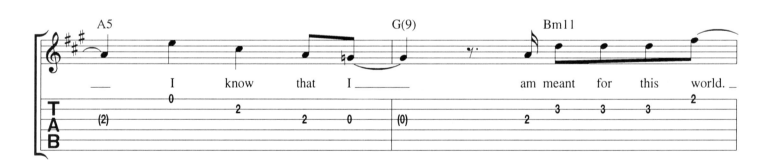

Verse 2:
w/Rhy. Fig. 1 *(Gtr. 2) 4 times*

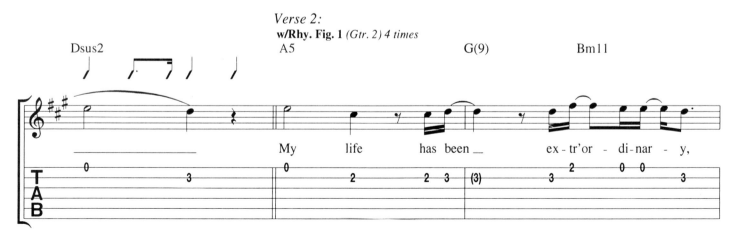

Muzzle – 7 – 2
PG9703

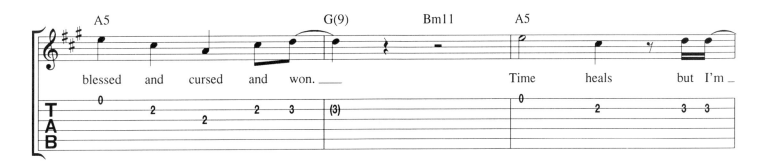

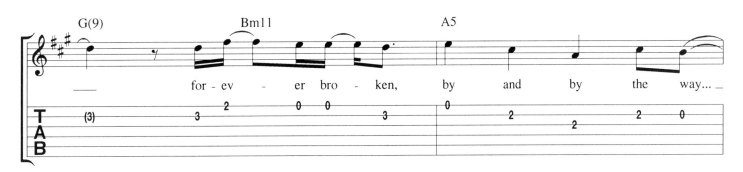

Pre-Chorus 2:

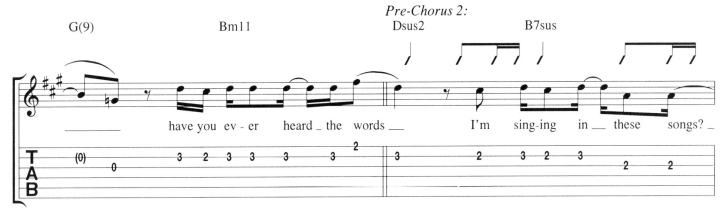

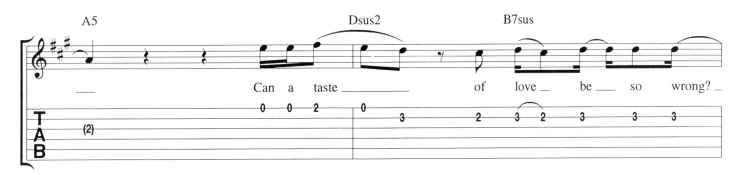

Muzzle – 7 – 3
PG9703

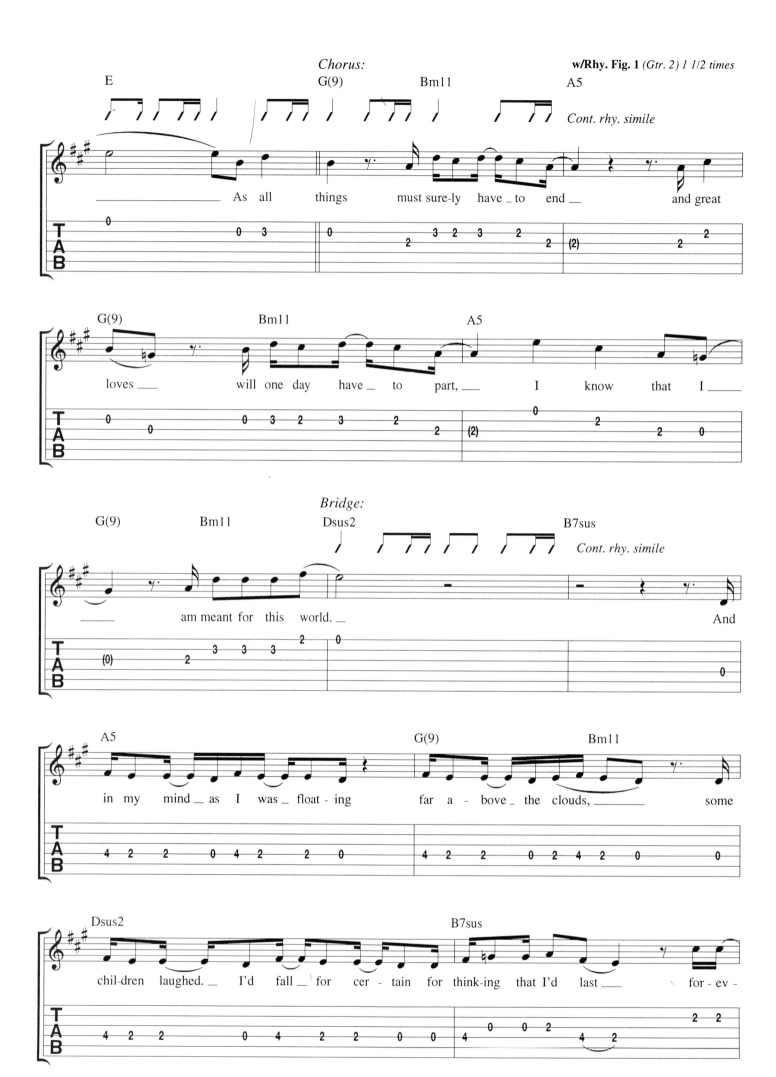

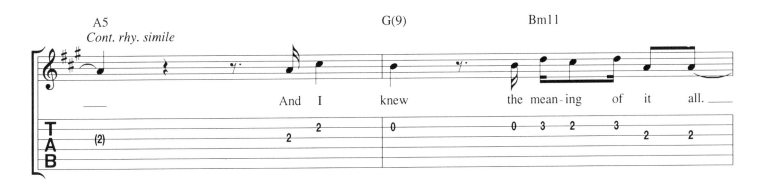

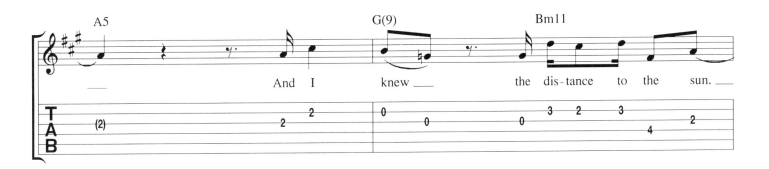

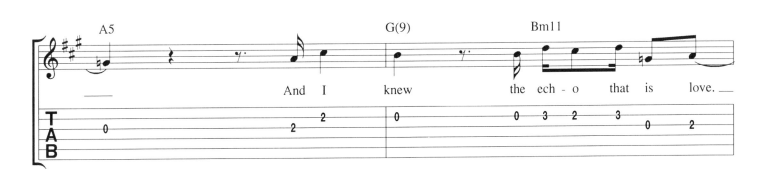

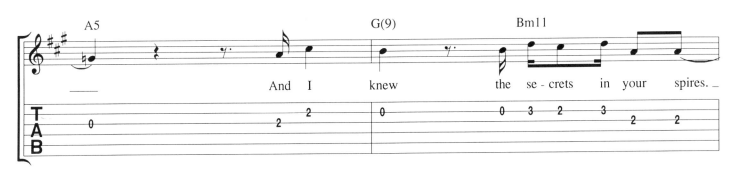

Muzzle – 7 – 5
PG9703

39

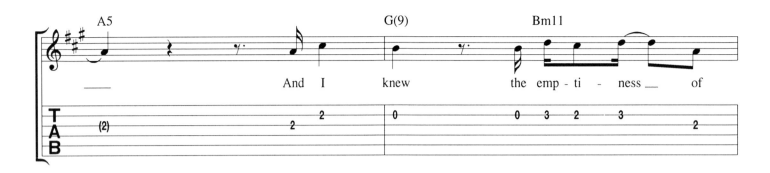

And I knew the emp - ti - ness _ of

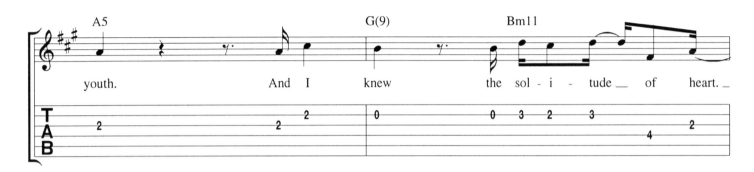

youth. And I knew the sol - i - tude _ of heart. _

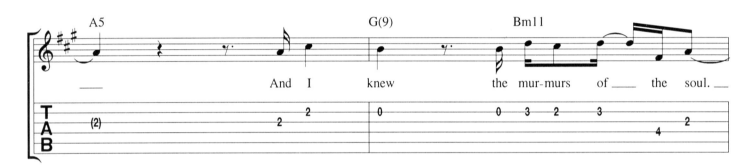

And I knew the mur-murs of ___ the soul. _

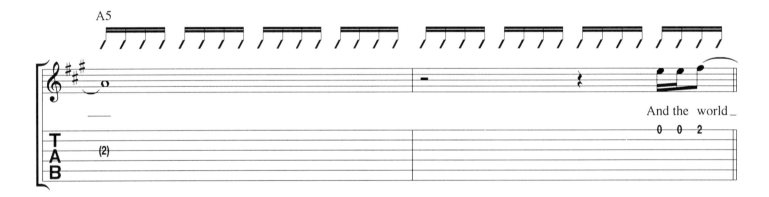

And the world _

Pre-Chorus 3:

is drawn in - to ___ your hands. _ And the world _
so hard to un - der - stand _ is the world _

1979

Words & Music by Billy Corgan

© Copyright 1995 MCA Music Limited, 77 Fulham Palace Road, London W6 8JA.

1979 – 6 – 2
PG9703

Forgotten and absorbed

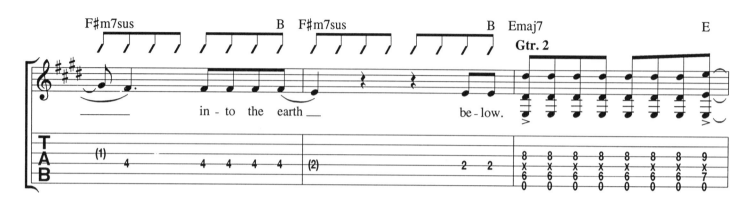

into the earth below.

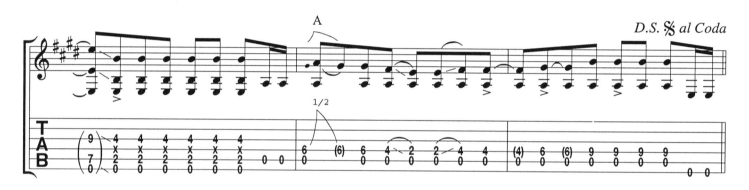

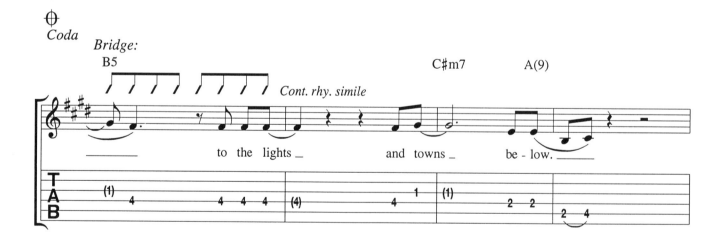

to the lights and towns below.

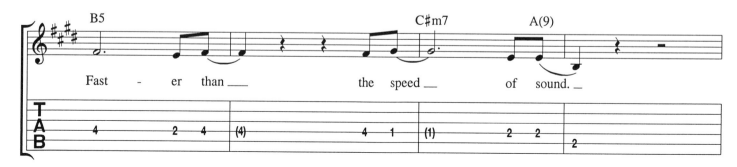

Fast - er than the speed of sound.

Verse 4:
w/Rhy. Fig. 1 *(Gtr. 2) 4 times*

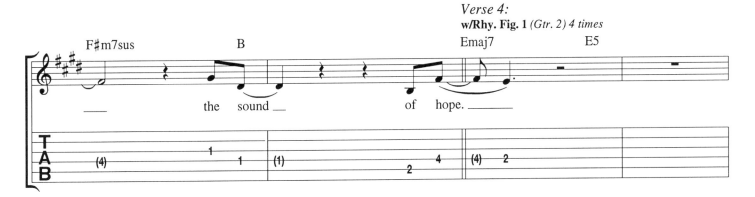

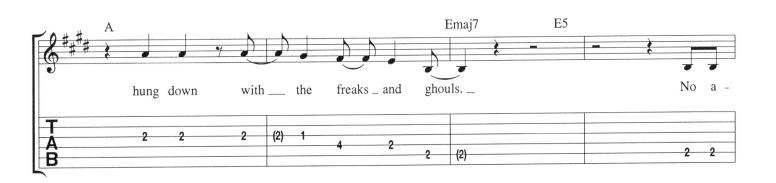

Chorus:
w/Rhy. Fig. 2 (Gtr. 2) 3 times

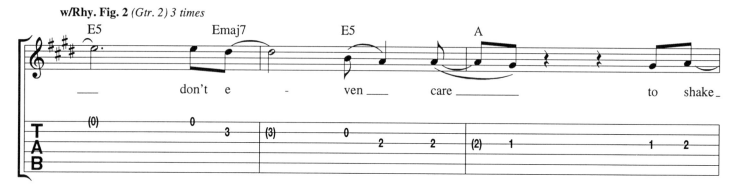

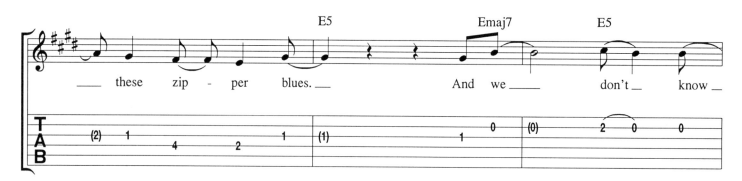

1979 – 6 – 5
PG9703

46

Verse 2:
Junebug skipping like a stone.
With the headlights pointed at the dawn.
We were sure we'd never see an end to it all.
(Chorus 1:)

Verse 3:
Double-cross the vacant and the bored.
They're not sure what we have in store.
Morphine city slippin' dues down to see. . .

Chorus 2:
That we don't even care,
As restless as we are,
We feel the pull
In the land of a thousand guilts.
And poured cement,
Lamented and assured
To the lights and towns below.

Spaceboy

Words & Music by Billy Corgan

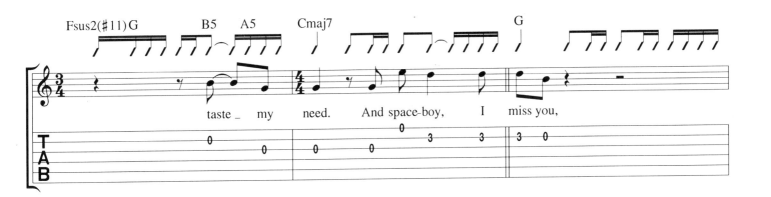

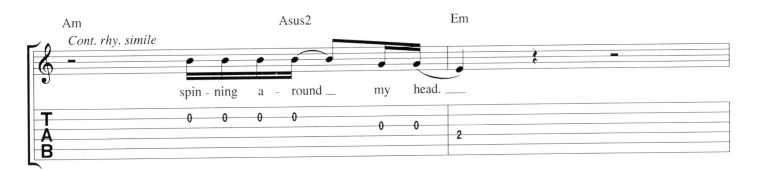

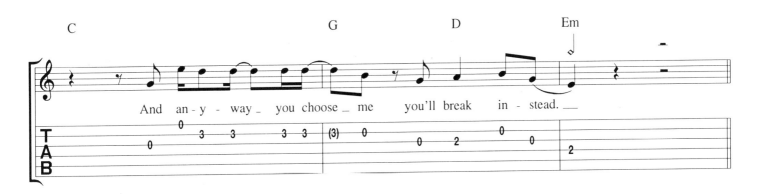

Verse 2:

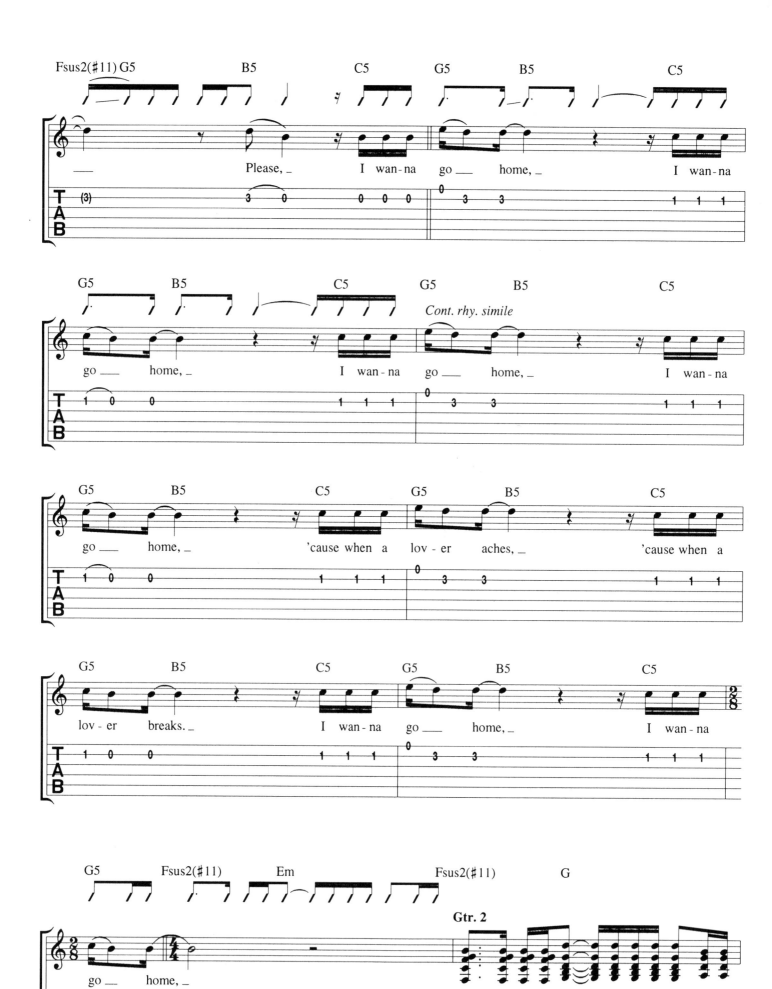

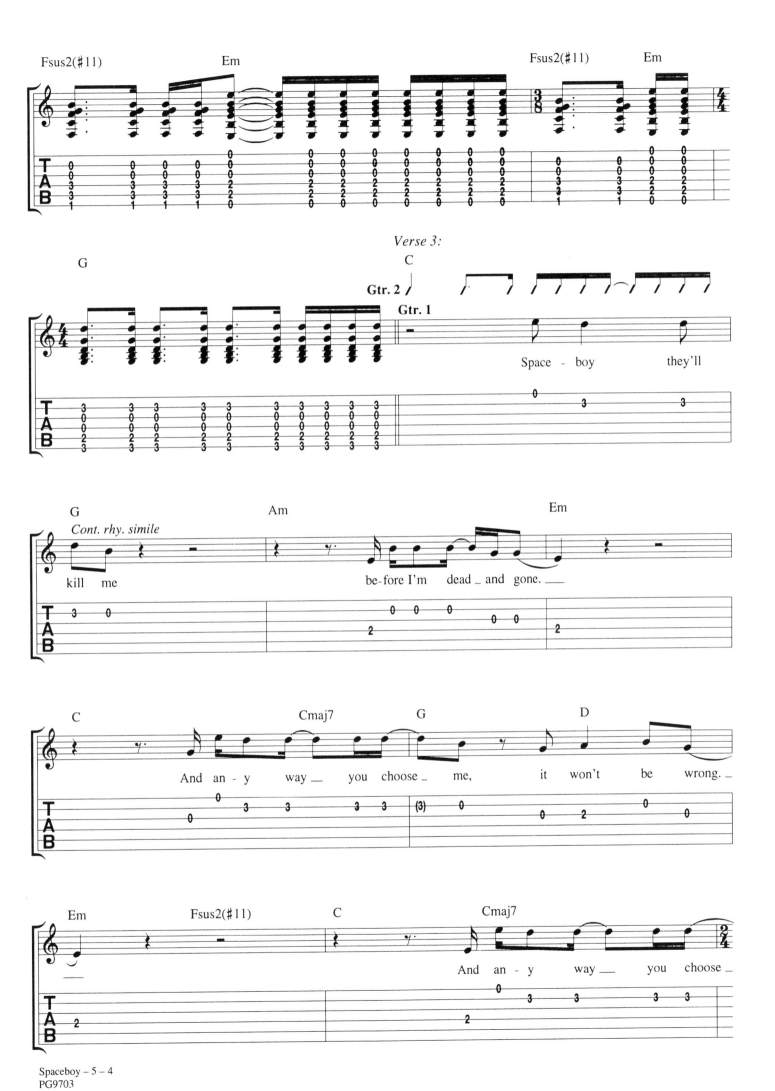

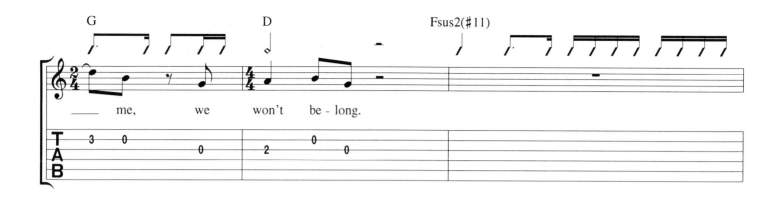

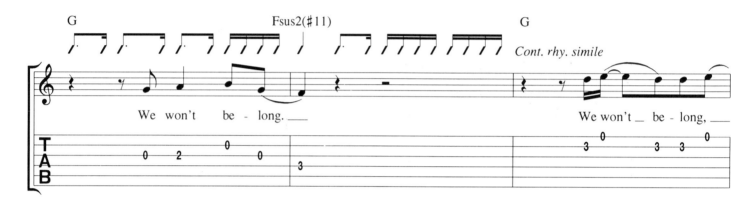

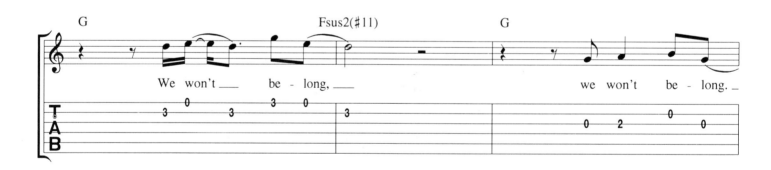

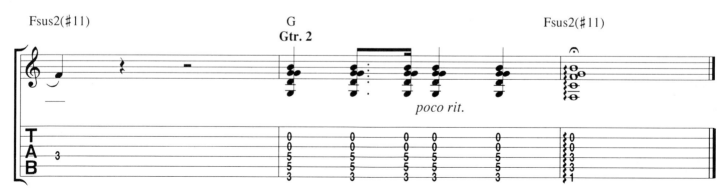

Thirty-Three

Words & Music by Billy Corgan

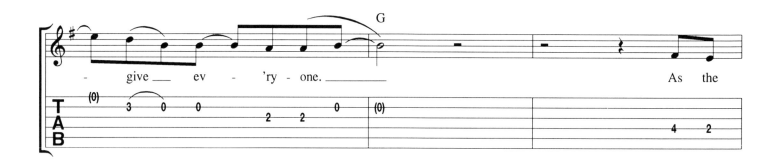

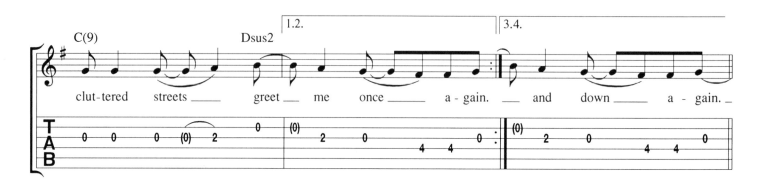

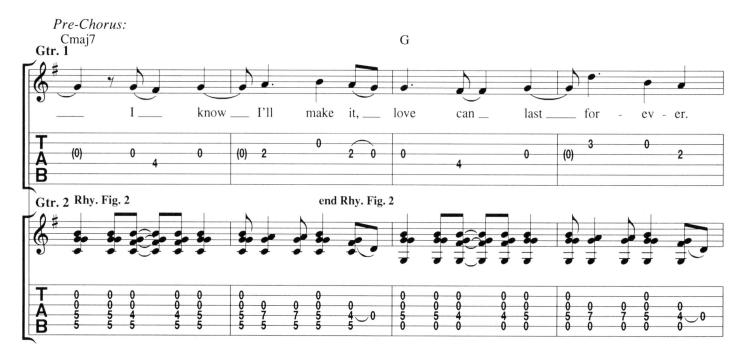

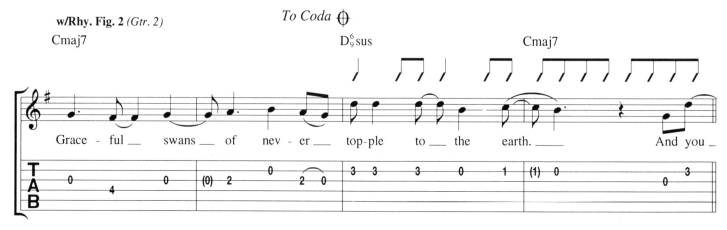

Thirty-Three – 5 – 2
PG9703

Chorus 1:
w/Rhy. Fig. 1 *(Gtr. 2) 3 times, simile*

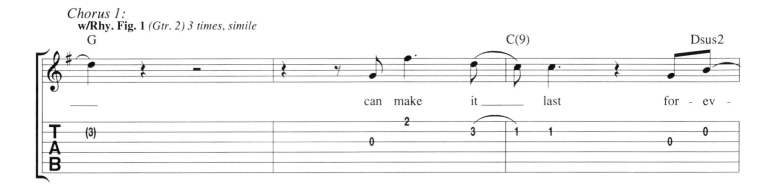

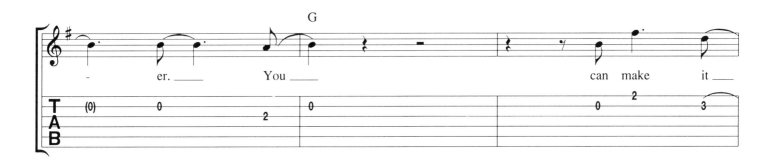

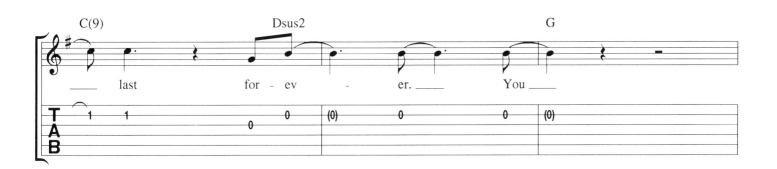

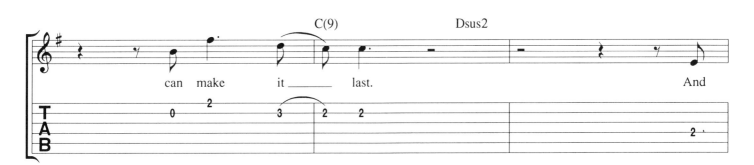

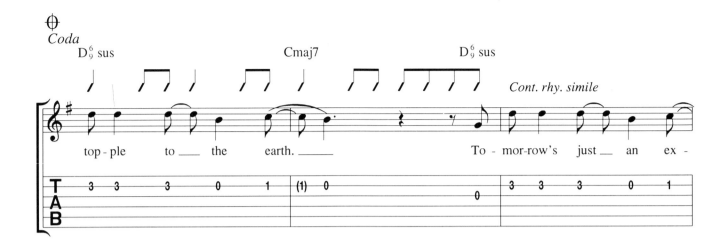

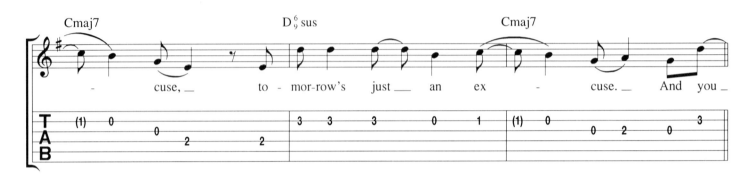

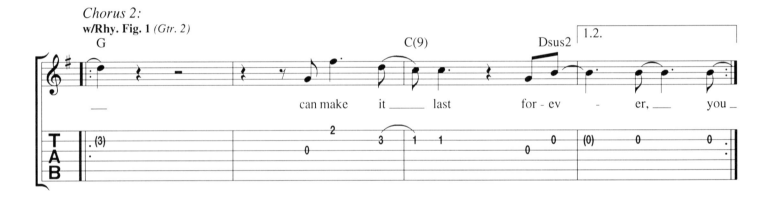

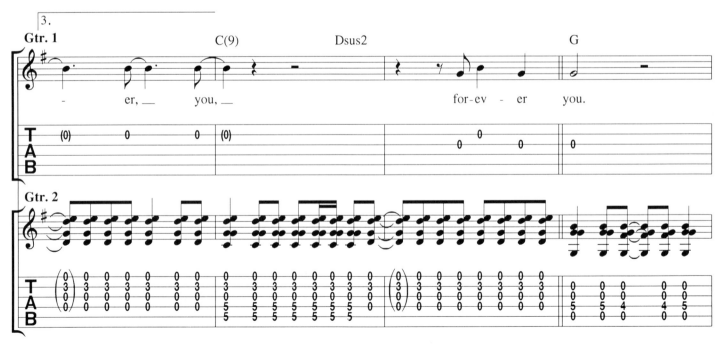

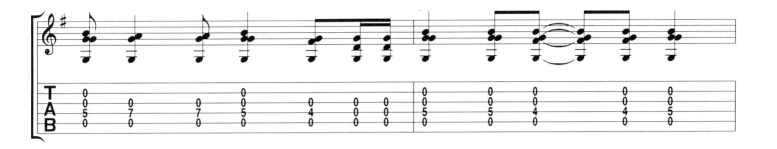

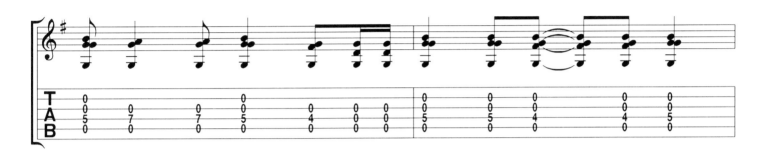

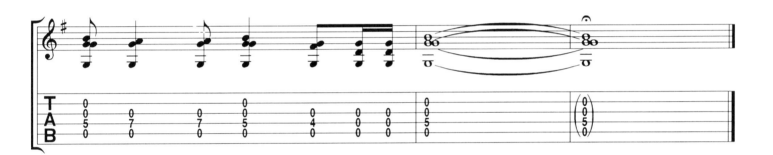

Verse 2:
I know I can't be late,
Supper's waiting on the table.
Tomorrow's just an excuse away.
So, I pull my collar up and face the cold,
On my own.

Verse 3:
The earth laughs beneath my heavy feet,
At the blasphemy in my own jangly walk.
Steeple, guide me to my heart and home.
The sun is out and up, and down again.
(To Pre-Chorus:)

Verse 4:
I've journeyed here and there, and back again.
But in the same old haunts, I still find my friends.
Mysteries not ready to reveal.
Sympathies I'm ready to return.
I'll make the effort, love can last forever...
(To Pre-Chorus:)

Today

Words & Music by Billy Corgan

© Copyright 1993 MCA Music Limited, 77 Fulham Palace Road, London W6 8JA.
All Rights Reserved. International Copyright Secured.

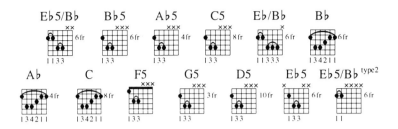

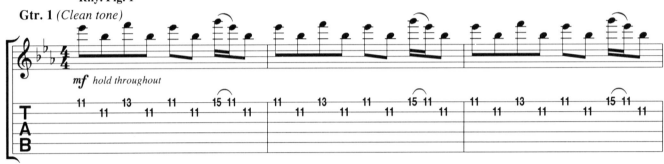

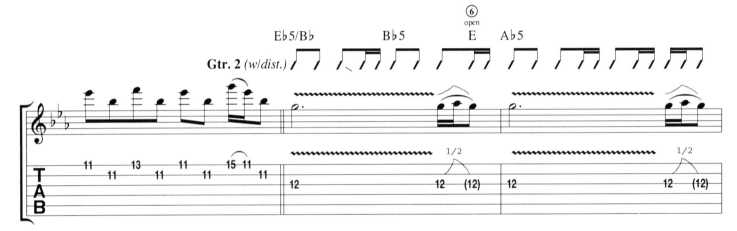

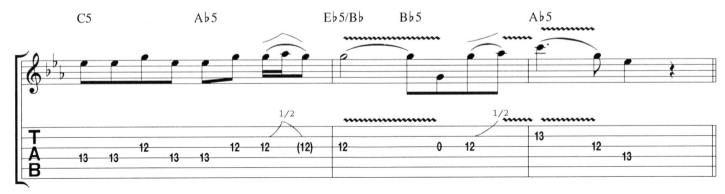

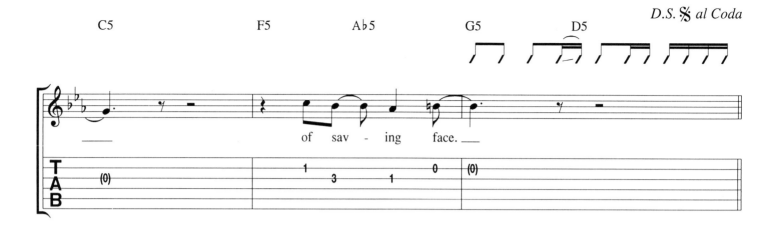

of sav - ing face.

⊕ *Chorus:*
Coda

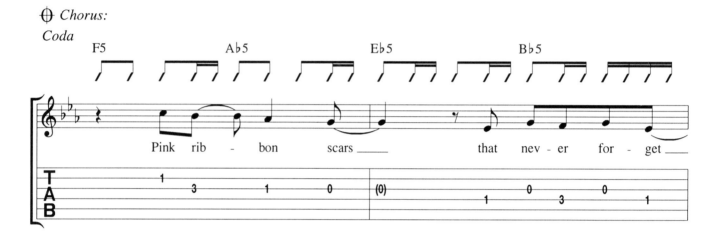

Pink rib - bon scars that nev - er for - get

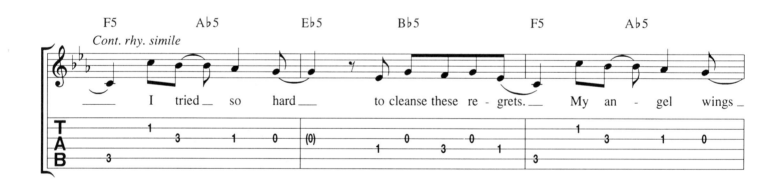

Cont. rhy. simile

I tried so hard to cleanse these re - grets. My an - gel wings

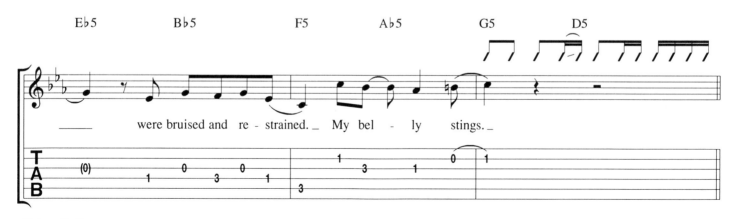

were bruised and re - strained. My bel - ly stings.

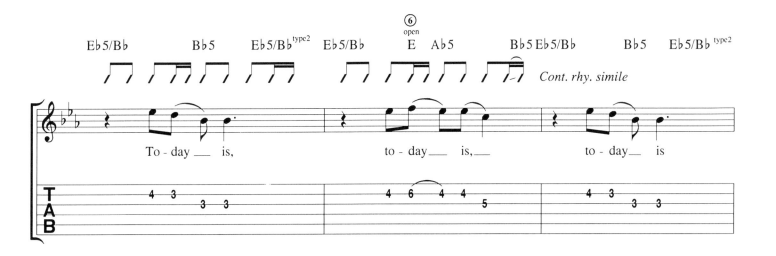

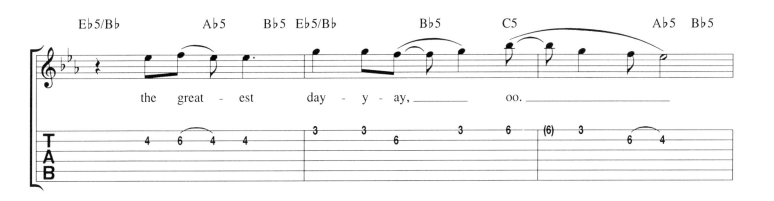

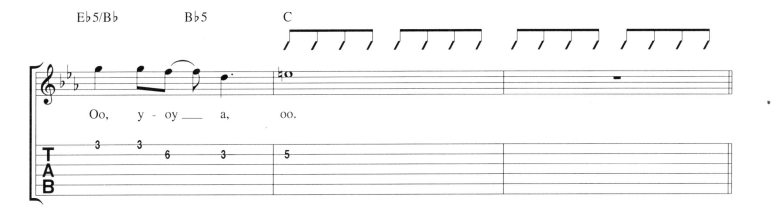

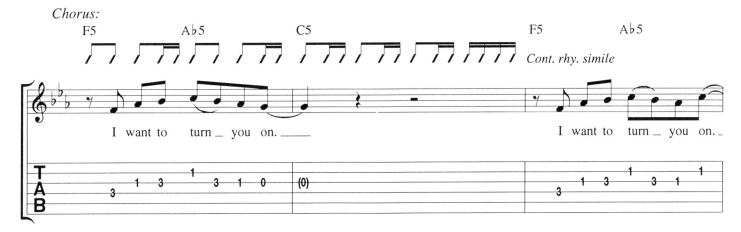

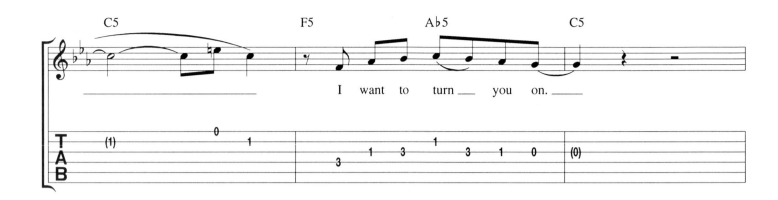

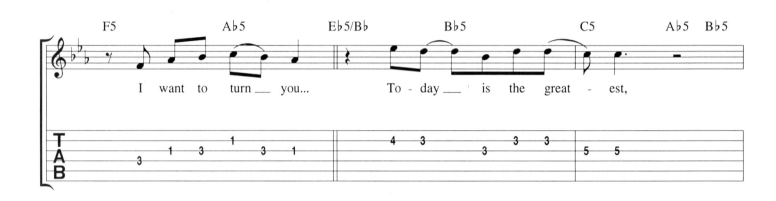

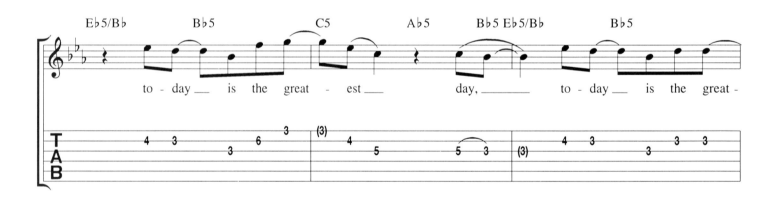

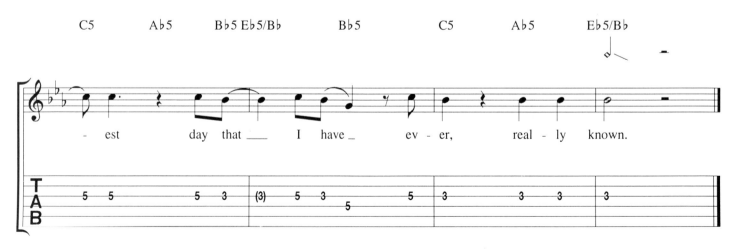

Tonight, Tonight

Words & Music by Billy Corgan

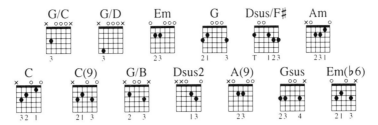

Tune down 1/2 step to match recording:

⑥ = E♭   ③ = G♭
⑤ = A♭   ② = B♭
④ = D♭   ① = E♭

Moderately uptempo rock ♩ = 152

Intro:

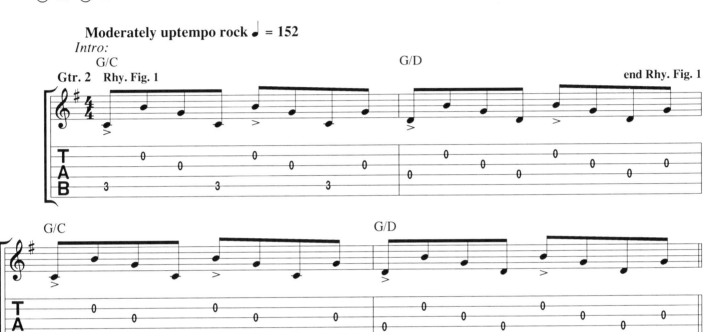

Verse 1:

w/Rhy. Fig. 1 *(Gtr. 2) 3 times*

Time   is   nev - er   time ___   at   all. ___   You   can

nev - er, ev - er   leave ___   with - out ___   leav - ing a piece ___

Tonight, Tonight – 7 – 1
PG9703

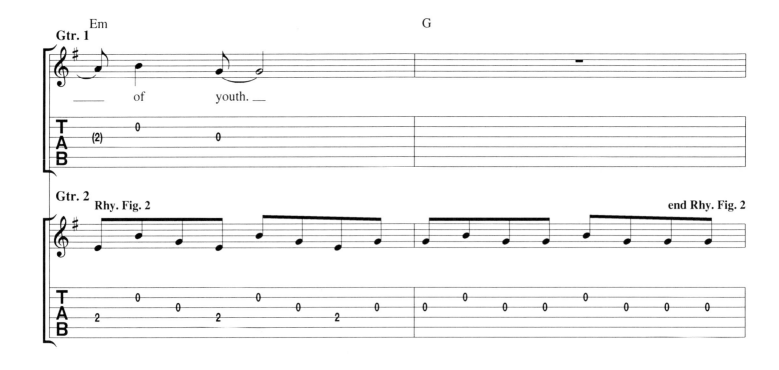

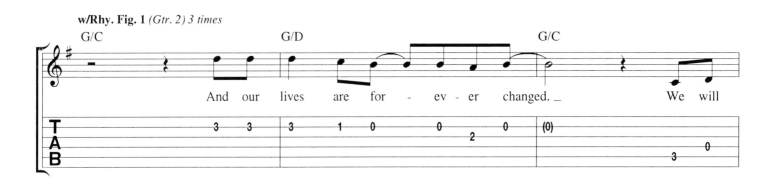

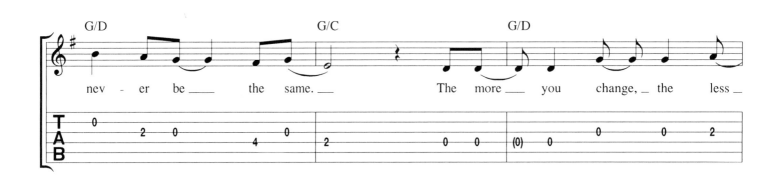

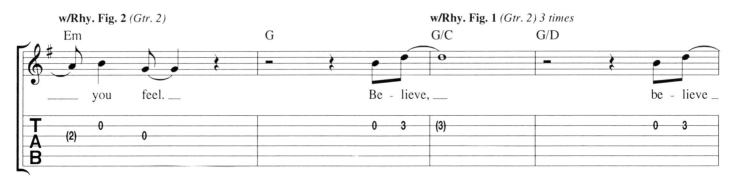

Tonight, Tonight – 7 – 2
PG9703

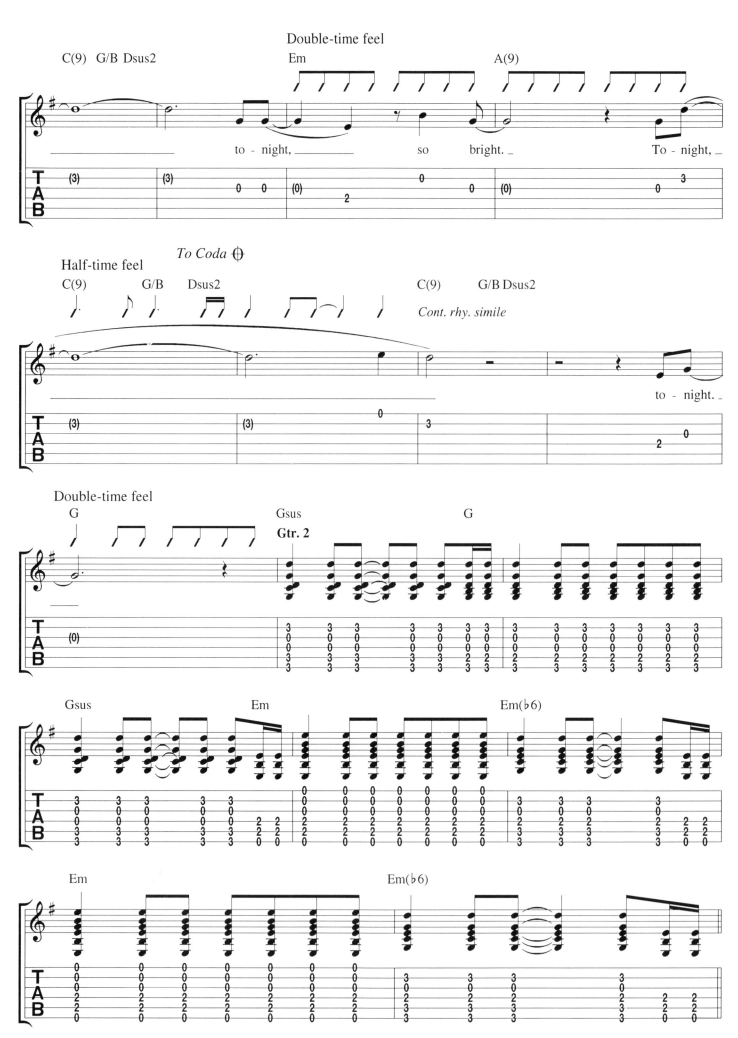

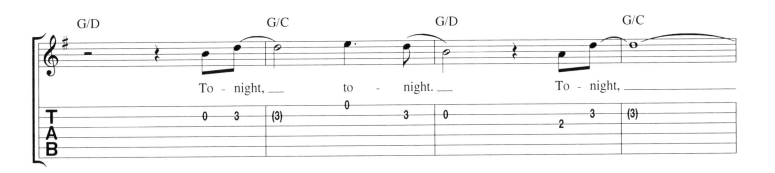

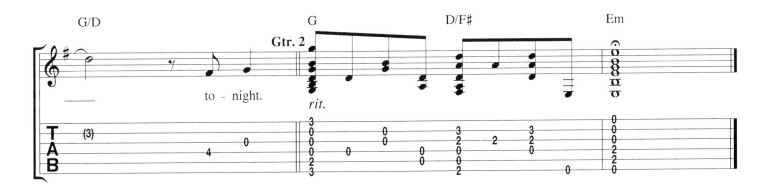

Coda:
We'll find a way to offer up the night, tonight.
The indescribable moments of your life, tonight.
The impossible is possible tonight, tonight.
Believe in me as I believe in you, tonight.

Guitar Tab Glossary

TABLATURE EXPLANATION

READING TABLATURE: Tablature illustrates the six strings of the guitar. Notes and chords are indicated by the placement of fret numbers on a given string(s).

String ⑥, 3rd Fret   String ① 12th Fret   A "C" Chord   C Chord Arpeggiated
String ③ 13th Fret

BENDING NOTES

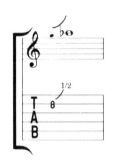

HALF STEP: Play the note and bend string one half step.*

PREBEND AND RELEASE: Bend the string, play it, then release to the original note.

WHOLE STEP: Play the note and bend string one whole step.

RHYTHM SLASHES

STRUM INDICA-TIONS: Strum with indicated rhythm.
The chord voicings are found on the first page of the transcription underneath the song title.

INDICATING SINGLE NOTES USING RHYTHM SLASHES: Very often single notes are incorporated into a rhythm part. The note name is indicated above the rhythm slash with a fret number and a string indication.

*A half step is the smallest interval in Western music; it is equal to one fret. A whole step equals two frets.

**By Kenn Chipkin and Aaron Stang

ARTICULATIONS

HAMMER ON: Play lower note, then "hammer on" to higher note with another finger. Only the first note is attacked.

PULL OFF: Play higher note, then "pull off" to lower note with another finger. Only the first note is attacked.

LEGATO SLIDE: Play note and slide to the following note. (Only first note is attacked).

PALM MUTE: The note or notes are muted by the palm of the pick hand by lightly touching the string(s) near the bridge.

ACCENT: Notes or chords are to be played with added emphasis.

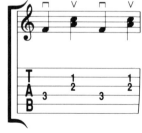

DOWN STROKES AND UPSTROKES: Notes or chords are to be played with either a downstroke (⊓ ⸳) or upstroke (∨) of the pick.

2/00 (36508)

Make
great music
straight away
with this
easy-to-play
series...

for *easy guitar* tab

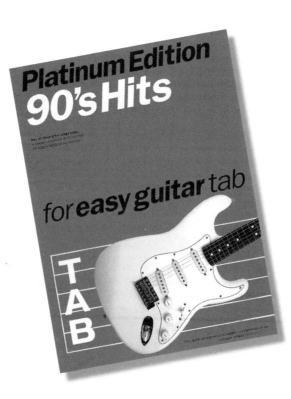